Construction Budgeting

Frank W. Helyar, FRICS, PQS (F)

Canadian Institute of Quantity Surveyors
P.O. Box 124, Station R, Toronto, Ontario M4G 3Z3

Construction Budgeting

ISBN # 1-896606-26-1, 2nd edition, 1998

(ISBN # 1-896606-10-5, 1st edition, 1993)

ACKNOWLEDGEMENTS

I wish to acknowledge with thanks the help given by Mr. James G.A. Gibbs, C.A. in updating Chapter 11.

As well I wish to thank Clare, Randall-Smith & Associates for providing all the information contained in

Appendix B along with Gordon Pattison PQS and Evan Stregger PQS who read the manuscript and made

helpful comments and suggestions. Thanks also to Larry Barclay PQS who, while preparing for the Institute's

examinations, discovered a few errors and took the time to write to me. I have noted his suggestions and made

the necessary corrections.

I take the view, and always have done, that if you cannot say what you have to say in twenty minutes, you should go away and write a book about it.

Lord Brabazon of Tara

Contents

CONSTRUCTION BUDGETING

FOREWORD

About the Author

It is appropriate that this introduction to the author should be written by a Canadian born and trained quantity surveyor who has directly benefitted from the contributions that Frank Helyar has made to the Canadian Quantity Surveying profession.

It is not only appropriate, but an honour.

Frank Helyar was born in London, England in 1927. He received his early education there graduating from the City of London School. After national service with the British Army he articled with a British firm of quantity surveyors, Eric G. Lynde & Partners. This led to his election, following examination, to the Royal Institution of Chartered Surveyors.

Anticipating the opportunities available in a young, dynamic country Frank emigrated to Canada in 1954. He met his wife, Joy, a school teacher, and settled down in Toronto to raise a family of one daughter and three sons. He undoubtedly did not realize it at the time, but Frank was also beginning to change the face of the Canadian construction industry.

Frank's first job in Canada proved to be his only job as the employee of a firm, other than his own. He joined the prominent architectural firm of Marani & Morris in their in-house estimating department. During his four years there he established contacts with numerous other quantity surveyors from various Commonwealth countries. These contacts led to the initial meetings of what was to become the Canadian Institute of Quantity Surveyors.

In 1958, Frank sensed the need for a new type of consulting quantity surveyor and started up in his own practice. While other professional quantity surveying firms had recently set up in Canada, Frank's was the first to promote and use the now widely established Elemental Cost Analysis system, a system which he was instrumental in designing.

Today, the firm currently known as Helyar & Associates is one of Canada's largest quantity surveying practices. It has produced many accomplished quantity surveyors, many of whom are playing an important role in the profession throughout Canada.

In 1959 the Canadian Institute of Quantity Surveyors was incorporated. Frank was its first secretary. In 1962 he became its third president. He was one of the first members to receive a CIQS Fellowship and its Award of Merit, both of which acknowledge his significant contributions to the Institute and the development of quantity surveying in Canada. Frank has continually contributed to the organization in one capacity or another, including the updating of this book.

Frank has served as the President of both the Ontario Association of Consulting Quantity Surveyors which was formed in 1973, and of the Ontario Institute of Quantity Surveyors which was founded in 1974.

In addition to being a major figure in the establishment of our relatively new profession, Frank has lectured on the subject of Quantity Surveying and Construction Economics at various universities and colleges, including Pennsylvania State University, University of Toronto, University of Waterloo and Niagara College. He has also participated in the OAA registration course lectures, and contributed many articles to various construction publications.

In 1992, after a long and successful career he retired from his company. He continues to promote quantity surveying in Canada.

Arthur W. Hooker, PQS (F)
October 1993

INTRODUCTION

This book is an updating of *Construction Estimating and Costing* first published in 1979 by McGraw-Hill Ryerson. The original was based on a series of lectures to architects on the subject of Construction Economics covering what is now Part One of this book, expanded to include most of the chapters in Part Two. It is hoped that it will be of interest to quantity surveyors, architects, contractors, developers and others connected with the construction industry, and that it will demonstrate some of the scope of training and experience required by quantity surveyors which makes them more than just construction estimators.

Quantity surveying is not yet the recognized profession in North America that it is in the United Kingdom, in parts of Europe, and in many of the Commonwealth countries. However, even in the United Kingdom it is a comparatively recent profession and although there are references in both the Bible[1] and Shakespeare[2] to work which might be construed as normally being performed by quantity surveyors, it was really only in the eighteenth century that quantity surveyors started to become identified as a separate entity, and only in the nineteenth century that they became recognized professionals.

Prior to the seventeenth century in England the design of buildings was generally confined to the drawing of a ground plan or `platte', usually by a surveyor but sometimes by one of the craftsmen. If the building were of some importance the surveyor, for an additional fee, would also provide an elevation or `upright'. The importance of the embryonic architect in those days can be judged by the following adjoining entries which can be found in the *Black Books of Lincoln's Inn* for 1561:

"1. Paid Potter the bricklayer for drawing the plans for the building the Inne 4s 0d
 2. Received a fine from Fleming for having his beard too long 3s 4d"

A copy of the plan was given to the craftsmen, each of whom worked in his own trade with his own men. They would record their time and send the bill to the building owner, rather like a present day cost plus project. On smaller jobs they usually sent their bills after the work was completed, but on larger jobs they were frequently paid a cash advance to be adjusted on completion. The owner, in addition to paying for the labour, would supply the workmen with the necessary materials to work with. If the owner were a religious body or a university it was likely that most of the stone and timber used in the construction would come from its own property.

If the building were important and large enough the work would be under the general co-ordinating supervision of a building surveyor who was usually a master mason or carpenter, the mason probably belonging to the fraternity of Freemasons. He was a man of some standing and if he were sufficiently well known he might have several buildings under his control. He would visit each in turn, laying out the work and doing some of the more intricate details himself, while his apprentices and the workmen who would complete the job looked on or worked under his guidance.

Inigo Jones is credited with importing from Italy the concept of having an architect design and supervise the building from beginning to end and with it came the Italian Method of having a single contractor to superintend the work and pay the craftsmen. His Banqueting Hall in London's Whitehall, built in 1620, was probably the last of the great buildings to be built by individual craftsmen, although the old practice continued for lesser buildings into the nineteenth century, while Lincoln's Inn Chapel, designed in the same year, was built by a single contractor. At this time too the designation of architect began to replace that of surveyor, although to this day some of the London guilds still retain a surveyor to the guild, a position usually occupied by an architect.

---

[1] Luke 14: 28-30

[2] Henry IV Part II

Despite the changes brought about by Inigo Jones it was still customary for the contractor to be paid in advance for at least some of the work, and for the building owner to supply the materials. Payments were made during the course of construction on a weekly or monthly basis, either on the cost of wages expended or by measurement of the amount of work done.

Where payment was to be made on measurement rather than on the actual time spent, unit rates were agreed upon between the workmen or the contractor and the owner, usually with the architect acting as the owner's representative. Most often the unit rates were agreed before construction started but sometimes they were negotiated when the work was finished. The architect was responsible for agreeing measurements and would often employ a measurer or measuring surveyor to do so, although some architects used clerks or pupils to do the work. No doubt the clerks and pupils were not particularly interested in this type of work because in time the workmen became dissatisfied with this arrangement and employed their own measuring surveyor to look after their interests.

The job of a measuring surveyor was not at that time considered to be a very elevated one, and many of the surveyors had a poor reputation for accuracy and honesty. There was no formal training for them, and very little in the way of books to guide them. In 1663 Sir Balthazar Gerbier produced his book *Counsel and Advice to all Builders* which contained long schedules of prices but was said to be a superficial and padded work. Stephen Primatt published his *City and Country Purchaser and Builder* in 1667, the year following the Great Fire of London. He gave as his reason for doing so the fact that:

"Many of those wanting to build are compelled to trust to the Fidelity of Workmen and Surveyors who have been observed to make a harvest in the Citie Ruines and combine together to take excessive Rates for their work which hath discouraged many . . . The purchaser is oft-times over-reached by the seller and thereby undone."

Prior to this the Carpenters' Rule for the easy measuring of `superficies and solids' had been devised, and Leonard Digges had published *A Book Named Tectonicon* in 1556 `for the exact measuring and speedie reckoning all manner of Land, Square, Timber, Stone, Steeples, Pillars, Globes etc.' with an instrument known, ominously, as a `profitable staff'. It was, in fact, the first theodolite or transit.

Another reason for the poor reputation enjoyed by measuring surveyors could have been the transient nature of the business. Keat's *London Directories* lists the unusual name of Ezekiel Delight as Oil and Colourman in 1779, as a builder shortly afterwards, and as a surveyor in 1794.

Two events occurred at the beginning of the nineteenth century which radically changed the construction industry, at least in southern England. The first was that, due to the Napoleonic wars, the government decreed that `on the score of economy and dispatch' all public building projects should be under the control of one contractor. This was, of course, already being done on major projects but it now became mandatory for projects of all sizes.

The second event was the demand for open competitive tendering. Whereas previously the total cost of the building was known only when the work was finished, owners now required that the contractors give a price before work started. One of the effects of this was that measurements had to be taken from the drawings before construction started rather than on the site after the work was completed, and as a result many of the old measuring surveyors, at least the more inefficient ones, soon found themselves out of work.

A book written by John Noble in 1836 describes the new system:

"An excellent system has been recently adopted by the Craft, in selecting a few respectable builders to tender for the performance of the work; then appointing one surveyor and the employer another, to ascertain the quantities together and to bring the same into blank account; so that each party proceeds to value the items upon the same accurate data, on which he founds his tender, and this mode is beneficial to them and the public."

At first this system required two or more surveyors to measure the quantities, a carry-over of the old practice where both parties measured the work for progress payments. In time, however, it came to be realized that this was rather inefficient and time-wasting and, as confidence in the skills and integrity of the surveyor grew, the contractors agreed to accept the quantities measured by a single surveyor to be appointed and paid by all the contractors who were submitting a tender and the requirement of a surveyor measuring on behalf of the owner was dropped. Later, to preserve secrecy in tendering, it was agreed that the architect on behalf of his client should appoint the surveyor. A relic of the old system survived until shortly after World War II when the successful contractor was required to pay the quantity surveyor's fee, having included the amount in his tender.

The schedules of labour and materials on which the contractors based their tenders became known as bills of quantities, and the surveyor changed from being a measuring surveyor to being a quantity surveyor. Together with the change in name, quantity surveying became an independent profession about the middle of the nineteenth century. In 1872 the report of a special committee to the General Conference of Architects on the employment of surveyors recommended that a single surveyor nominated by the architect should be employed to prepare the bills of quantities rather than have the architect do it himself. It also recommended that the bills of quantities should form part of the contract, to be used for adjusting the contract price when changes are made in the work. Even so, as late as 1880 quantities and competitive tendering were still being described in some quarters as "the modern system of contracting and tendering for work".

The profession has evolved gradually over the past 150 years, with many major changes taking place in the last 50 years. When the bills of quantities are being prepared by an independent quantity surveyor it is essential for the contractors to know exactly how they have been measured and what has been included in each of the work items. Early on, quantity surveying firms established guidelines for the use of the contractors, but these would vary from firm to firm and from location to location. In 1922 the Royal Institution of Chartered Surveyors and the National Federation of Building Trades Employers jointly published *The Standard Method of Measurement of Building Works* which gave uniform guidelines and provided consistency of measurement throughout England and Wales. This document has passed through several editions, major revisions having taken place with each new edition, and since the 1950s has also been accepted in Scotland. Other publications covering engineering works and small building works are now also available.

Bills of quantities need to be organized into trades to be of use to the contractor when preparing a tender. The normal practice is for general contractors to price the quantities for their own work and to send copies of the quantities to those sub-trades from whom they wish to receive a price. None of them will measure the quantities but will accept them as being accurate. Competition is therefore solely on price. At tender closing only lump sum prices are submitted, but the lowest bidder will be required to provide fully priced bills of quantities to the quantity surveyor within a given period of time, usually 24 or 48 hours, for checking. Any arithmetical or other errors are adjusted and, provided the tender is still the lowest, the contractor will be awarded the contract. If the corrected price puts it above the next lowest bidder the contractor is given the option of standing by the tender or making the correction. Unless the error is a major one the contractor will usually stand by its tender since the contract will likely be awarded to the next bidder if the correction is made. When the price has been settled and the contract signed, the priced bills of quantities becomes one of the contract documents, to be used for adjusting the cost of changes in the work during construction. However, only the low tenderer is required to reveal its unit prices, and then only to the quantity surveyor. This is to prevent an unscrupulous architect or building owner going through the priced bills of quantities and making changes during construction to the detriment of the contractor.

Besides using the unit prices in the bills of quantities for adjusting the cost of changes in the work during construction, they are also used for correcting any errors in the quantities which may subsequently be found. The contractor accepts the quantities as being accurate at the time of tendering, but if it is discovered later that an item was under-measured the contractor is entitled to claim an extra to correct the error. In theory the contractor should also submit a credit if it is found the item was over-measured. Since the error is adjusted at the unit price contained in the bills of quantities the owner should have no hesitation in accepting it because, in theory at least, the low tender would have been higher by that amount if the error had not been made.

Quantity surveyors have progressed a long way from the old measuring surveyors of the eighteenth century. Measuring surveyors were all men whereas today many women are to be found in the profession. The quantity surveyor's role has also expanded and besides preparing bills of quantities they are responsible for negotiating the cost of changes in the work and settling the final account, and for valuing the progress payments, although it is still the architect's responsibility to issue the certificate of payment each month on the recommendation of the quantity surveyor. Because of the cost expertise they have acquired, quantity surveyors have become not only the technical accountants of the construction industry, but are also used extensively to advise the building owner on probable costs of construction in the pre-tender stages, using cost planning and cost control techniques developed since the Second World War. Many firms now also rely very heavily on computers for all aspects of their work.

NORTH AMERICA

In North America the quantity surveying profession has not evolved in the same way as it has in Britain. While Australia, New Zealand and other parts of the Commonwealth have adopted the British system with some local modifications, and even parts of Europe have adopted the bills of quantities system in recent years, North America remains virtually the last English-speaking area where quantity surveying is not a generally recognized profession.

Because the contractors and sub-contractors have to measure their own quantities when tendering a project, most quantity surveyors are employed on their staffs rather than acting as independent consultants. The last thirty years has, however, seen the emergence of a number of firms of independent quantity surveyors who offer pre-tender cost advice to architects and building owners, using the cost planning and cost control techniques developed in Britain. They also offer other services usually associated with quantity surveying such as giving expert evidence or acting as an arbitrator in disputes about construction costs, providing replacement costs for appraisers, and mortgage appraisals and financial supervision on behalf of banks and real estate investors.

In 1959 the Canadian Institute of Quantity Surveyors was formed in Toronto. Its principal aims are to provide a means of communication between quantity surveyors, to act as a spokesman for its members, and to act as an examining body for those who wish to become quantity surveyors. This last role has required the establishment of a course of studies and the investigation of various educational institutions together with the offer of advice and encouragement to potential members.

In recent years, because Canada is such a large country, it was decided to create autonomous provincial associations which are affiliated with the Canadian Institute of Quantity Surveyors. Currently they are the Quantity Surveyors Society of British Columbia, the Association of Quantity Surveyors of Alberta, the Ontario Institute of Quantity Surveyors, the Quantity Surveyors of Quebec Incorporated, the Nova Scotia Association of Quantity Surveyors and the Newfoundland and Labrador Association of Quantity Surveyors. Outside these provinces the Canadian Institute of Quantity Surveyors is still the body governing the affairs of quantity surveyors.

The Ontario Association of Consulting Quantity Surveyors was founded in 1974 as an association of consulting firms which supports the aims and objectives of the Canadian Institute of Quantity Surveyors, but which is intended to protect the interests of those firms in private practice in Ontario. Although Ontario is the only province having a formal association of consulting quantity surveyors, they are to be found in most major cities in Canada.

Canadian quantity surveyors have found a place for themselves in the construction industry over the past thirty years. They may not prepare bills of quantities as their counterparts in other parts of the world do, but they are able to provide all the other services offered by quantity surveyors elsewhere.

UNITS of MEASUREMENT

Since the Canadian construction industry has largely converted to the SI system of measurement the examples in this book are in metric. However, the principles described are equally applicable to buildings designed under the imperial system merely by substituting feet or yards for metres.

Conversion Table								
m^2	x	10.7639	=	sf	x	.0929	=	m^2
m^3	x	1.0380	=	cy	x	.7600	=	m^3
m	x	3.2808	=	ft	x	.3048	=	m
mm	x	.3097	=	in	x	25.4	=	mm

PART 1

Construction Cost Planning and Cost Control

CHAPTER 1

The Need for Cost Control

In the past, when architects were asked to give an estimate on a building they were designing, they would usually measure its floor area or volume and multiply the result by a unit price obtained from previous projects of a similar type. Since buildings differ greatly in design and methods of construction they had to be very careful in the selection of the unit price and would often check it with a friendly contractor.

This may have been satisfactory a hundred years ago when construction techniques were comparatively simple and not subject to major changes from year to year and from project to project, and when cost inflation was minimal. Today, however, building requirements have become more complicated and with all the new materials and construction techniques which are readily available, together with the extreme variation in prices which has taken place over the past few years, the possibility of costs getting out of control in the pre-tender period is far greater than it used to be. Nineteenth century pre-tender estimating techniques are no longer valid for this century, not only because they no longer give very accurate results, but also because they cannot be used to help control costs during the design stage.

The need for cost control will be viewed in different ways by the various parties to a construction project: the building owner, the architects and their consultants, and the contractor.

THE BUILDING OWNER

It almost goes without saying that building owners are greatly concerned with the cost of their proposed buildings. Besides wanting to be assured that the money allocated for the project at the conceptual stage is sufficient when tenders are opened, they would also like to feel that they are getting value for their money. For a prospective house owner the decision to build is one of the most important financial decision of his or her life, requiring an initial estimate which is as accurate as possible. Similarly, if the proposed structure is a speculative office building for which the developer has allocated a construction cost in the feasibility study, an increase of only a few per cent in the actual construction cost could mean the difference between success and disaster. Although the situation might not always be so critical, most prospective owners, whether private clients or government departments, have a very real concern that costs stay within their budgets.

Despite the fact that cost control can be crucial to the building owner it is not unknown for tenders to be opened and found to be higher than the owner and the design consultants had expected. This leaves the owner with four options:

1. The project is abandoned. This means that the owner will have been put to some expense without having a building to show for it, while the consultants will have suffered a loss in reputation as well as part of their fee.

2. The building is redesigned to meet the budget. This is a quite frequent but very unsatisfactory solution since a design which has been carefully thought out over a period of several months can only suffer if it has to be radically changed within a few days or weeks. The owner is upset because of the disruption to the schedule and possible extra expense caused by the delay, and the design team is put to additional work and expense without any increase in its fee.

   The current *Standard Form of Agreement between Client and Architect* issued by the Ontario Association of Architects requires the architect to prepare a final estimate of cost, to be agreed by the client, just prior to calling tenders. If the low tender exceeds this estimate by a certain percentage, usually 10%, the architect must redesign the project to bring the cost down to an

1

acceptable level. The architect's fee is then based on the revised tender price, unless the changes result in a cost which is less than the final estimate, in which case it is based on the final estimate.

3. The consultants are fired and new ones brought in who, the owner hopes, will do a better job of cost control. This option will result in delay and additional expense for the owner and a loss of fees and reputation for the original consultants.

4. The owner finds more money to cover the extra expense. In this case the owner will likely have to re-arrange the financing for the project and may own an architectural monument when the building is complete. Occasionally, despite irritation over the additional expense, the owner may feel that the resulting building was, in fact, worth it. After all, the financial problems of the owner are rarely considered when admiring the architectural qualities of a building and the cost of many notable buildings in the past have exceeded their architect's estimate. Nevertheless, it is irresponsible for an architect to design a building which is beyond the client's means.

Regardless of which course of action has to be taken the owner, because the consultants have paid insufficient attention to the costs, will be put to additional expense; either directly because of the increased cost of the project, or indirectly because of delay in construction, and time has a measurable value to most owners.

Tenders which are well below the budget can also be annoying to the building owner, although not to the same extent as tenders which exceed the budget. A larger or more elaborate building could have been designed and, although changes can be made to increase the scope during construction, this is not a very satisfactory solution.

Where the building is to be built under a management contract a construction manager is appointed, and the detailed design proceeds in sequence with the calling of trade package tenders as the building is being built. In this case (known as fast-track in the United States) the owner's options are reduced from four to two when costs start to exceed the budget. The project can hardly be abandoned if construction has already started, and it is unlikely that the owner would fire the consultants part-way through it. So the choices would be limited to having changes made in the design to reduce the cost of a trade package which has come in over budget, and to re-examine any trade packages which are still to be tendered; or the owner would have to find the extra money. Frequently, however, with a management contract there is sufficient flexibility to allow for those trades which have been over-estimated to compensate for those which have been under-estimated.

Although cost control is normally of great concern to the building owner, there are occasions when cost is only of secondary concern. Such circumstances arise when there is a difference between cost and value. Cost and value are often the same, but in some instances there may be a difference between them.

Many books and articles have been written on the theory of value. The true value of an object is not necessarily the value a person puts on it since that person may be ignorant or misinformed. It is more likely to be the price which can be obtained for it, although if only one person can be found who is prepared to pay the price it would still be a personal judgement, but at least they are prepared to back it up with their own money. If several people were prepared to pay the price it is unlikely they would all be ignorant or misinformed, so they could be considered to form a market which sets the market price and this would then establish the value. But the market may only be temporary, or limited, or even rigged, and may not be as well informed as it thinks it is. In the end, value is set by people's needs, which can vary from time to time. They will pay for what they believe they need or want at any given point in time, and value is therefore something which is constantly changing, varying as people's needs vary. It is often defined as the price which a willing buyer will pay a willing seller, each in normal competition with their peers, at a given point in time. Value will be discussed in more detail in later chapters since it is the criterion by which the economic feasibility of a project is judged, but it might be useful at this point to look at some examples where cost and value might appear to differ depending on the viewpoint of the owner.

If someone were to build a house at a cost of $500,000 this would be its value to them because that is what they were prepared to pay for it, and it satisfies their need at that time. If they then wanted to sell it on the open market and could only get $300,000 for it, the value to others is obviously less than its original cost.

A high-quality building in a poor locality, or a building which is out of scale with its community because of lack of judgement or the ignorance of the developer, is likely to have a value which is less than its cost. In the former case it sometimes happens that the construction of a superior building in a run-down community will spark general redevelopment in the area, and as a result the value may increase, although not necessarily enough to meet its cost. In the latter case a multi-storey building in a small town may be a very unwise investment since its cost could far exceed its value.

Where the building owner's principal business is something other than the ownership of the building, and the building is therefore of only secondary importance, the owner may be prepared to increase the construction cost beyond what might otherwise be considered reasonable in order to increase the value of the business. If for example, a major department store were to burn down, or if a manufacturer wanted to get a new product on the market as soon as possible, they would probably be willing to pay a premium for the construction because the value to them would be in having sales or manufacturing space available at the earliest possible moment, not in the physical value of the building.

While these examples give instances of cost apparently exceeding value, the reverse is normally true. The erection of a building on a raw piece of land is always intended to increase the value of the property, and an inexpensive parking structure on an existing parking lot, for example, could increase the income of the property, and hence its value, to a point well beyond the cost.

The relationship between cost and value is really in the realm of the appraiser and sometimes it can become quite complicated, but it is certainly of great concern to the building owner.

THE ARCHITECT

All that has been said about the building owner's concern with costs applies equally to architects and their consultants. They should be aware of the owner's concern and be prepared to respond accordingly. They should be able to assess the effect of any design changes on the cost so they can keep their client informed of his or her current financial commitments.

Not only can architects' reputations suffer if they pay no heed to costs, but any professional office needs at least to cover its own costs if it is to remain in business. To do so it should operate an internal cost control system, allocating portions of the anticipated fee to each stage in the design. Since professional fees are usually based on a percentage of the construction cost, any error in forecasting that cost can seriously upset the fee budget and affect the firm's profitability, particularly when tenders are found to be well below the budget.

The courts have had something to say about the position of an architect or engineer who makes an error in a pre-tender estimate, and the effect this can have on their fee. In *Fidias Consulting Engineering Ltd. v Jim Thymaras*, reported in *Construction Law Letter*, the engineer contracted to provide complete design, detailing, specifications and review of shop drawings of a restaurant for a percentage fee to be based on a pre-tender estimate, which the owner expected not to exceed $500,000, although the engineer claimed in court that the owner said it could go up to $1,000,000. The engineer started to prepare the contract documents and, before they were complete, estimated the project to be $900,000. He claimed that this was accepted by the owner as the pre-tender estimate on which his fee was to be based, while the owner claimed that he rejected the estimate and asked for changes to be made to reduce the cost. The owner also maintained that the engineer failed to make any changes, nor did he complete the contract documents. The engineer sued for the balance of his fee. Mr. Justice MacNaughton of the Queen's Bench of Alberta accepted the evidence of the owner and dismissed the engineer's claim on the grounds that, although negligence by the engineer had not been proved, the owner had indicated at the outset that he only wished to spend $500,000 on the project.

In *Gordon Shaw Concrete Products Ltd. v Design Collaborative Ltd.* the architects were retained to design a proto-type "earth-sheltered" house incorporating precast concrete panels manufactured by the plaintiff at a cost of about $60,000. This was to make them competitive with more traditional type houses in the area. The architects estimated the cost to be $60,144 based on a price per square foot. About a year later an experienced engineer was asked to provide an estimate and arrived at a figure in excess of $100,000, which the architects did not dispute. At this price the house was not competitive and the project was abandoned. The client sued the architects to recover the fee paid to them. The architects claimed that the house was a proto-type building of unique design and that costs could not be determined accurately until the project was tendered, but Mr. Justice Grant of the Supreme Court of Nova Scotia found the architects to be negligent and ordered them to refund their fee. On appeal in the Nova Scotia Court of Appeal the decision of the trial judge was upheld notwithstanding a clause in the standard form of architectural service contract stating that the architect did not warranty the accuracy of his estimates.

In both these cases a number of precedents were cited, starting with *Farnsworth v Garrard* in 1807, in which it was held that the architect could not recover payment for his services because:

1. The error in his estimate was due to his negligence, and
2. The client had derived no benefit from his services.

It has also been held that even if there is no mention of any budget restrictions in the contract between the architect and his client there is an implied agreement as to how much the project should cost if the architect knows that the client only has a certain amount to spend.

In *Saxby & Pokorny v Fowler* a clause in the agreement between the architect and his client read:

"When requested to do so, the Architect will prepare or procure preliminary estimates of the cost of the work, but does not guarantee the accuracy of such estimates and if requested he will review and if necessary revise such estimates from time to time as the preparation of drawings and specifications proceeds. Extra costs will only be determined when contract tenders are received."

This did not impress Mr. Justice Haddad of the Alberta Court of Appeal who said that despite the wording in the contract there is an implied condition that the final cost will be within reasonable range of the estimate. Similarly, in *Savage v Alberni School Trustees* Mr. Justice Smith of the British Columbia Court of Appeal said that if the architect provides an estimate as part of his contract it must be reasonably close to the ultimate cost, and if it isn't the architect must show how the error arose and that it was no fault of his.

The courts have also relied on *Hudson's Building and Engineering Contracts* in which it says:

"In the earliest stages of employment of his architect or engineer, the employer will in practice usually indicate or impose limitations on the cost of the proposed project. Even if no mention of this is made, it is suggested that an architect must design works capable of being carried out at a reasonable cost having regard to their scope and function. There will, therefore, in most cases be an express or implied condition of the employment that the project should be capable of being completed within a stipulated or reasonable cost, and an architect or engineer will be liable for negligence if, in fact, the excess cost is sufficient to show want of care or skill on his part."

A similar opinion is given in Sweet, *Legal Aspects of Architecture, Engineering and the Construction Process* as follows:

"If there is a cost condition, generally the architect gambles that his cost prediction will be reasonably accurate. If he is wrong, *whether negligent or not*, he loses his fee. If it is held that he promised to be accurate, he will be responsible for any damages which result from the inaccurate cost predictions."

These cases raise the question of how close a pre-tender estimate must be to the actual cost to be reasonable. In the past a reasonable margin of error of five per cent has been considered acceptable, but in *Mt. Cheam Developments v Clark* the figure was set at fifteen per cent. In this case Mt. Cheam Developments, a construction company, were hired by Dr. Clark to carry out renovations on an existing medical clinic. They examined the plans and toured the building and quoted $49,800 for the construction work. This was subsequently increased to $56,800 for additional work. When the project was completed Dr. Clark had paid the full $56,800 but the contractor said the job had in fact cost $85,486 and demanded the difference. In court, counsel for the contractor argued that the use of the word "estimate" and the brief wording of the written document demonstrated that there was no fixed-price contract and that "there was no meeting of minds between the parties" – meaning that there was no contract at all. The case should therefore be settled on the basis of "quantum meruit", a legal expression meaning as much as the contractor had earned. Mr. Justice Robinson of the Supreme Court of British Columbia accepted that "even though the contractor's assurance [that the project could be built for $56,800] cannot be said to be a warranty it was a representation upon which Dr. Clark could and did rely". There was no evidence that the renovation work was particularly difficult or unusual, or that the contractor had not been fully informed of what had to be done. The judge decided that it was not therefore unreasonable to hold the contractor to his estimate with an allowance "for those factors which the contractor could not reasonably have foreseen". He set this allowance at 15% and ruled that the contractor should be paid the amount of his estimate plus 15%, or $65,320.

THE CONTRACTOR

Contractors, although they are not usually consulted during the design of a building, have a rather indirect but nevertheless very real interest in pre-tender cost control. Their interest in cost control during construction, on the other hand, is very direct and sometimes at odds with the owner's interests.

Contractors and their sub-contractors are in business to make money. Tendering is a major overhead expense and contractors' estimating departments can represent 40% to 50% of their head office overhead. They therefore like to know that if they submit the lowest tender they will be building the project, while if their price is too high they can pass on to other tenders. If, because of insufficient cost control by the owner and the consultants, a contractor has to re-tender on a modified design, a disproportionate amount of the company's overhead will have been expended on the project. Worse still, if a contractor is low bidder and the project is cancelled because it is too expensive, it will have been wasting its time and will be wary about submitting tenders to that owner or those consultants in the future.

Further, when a building has to be redesigned to meet the budget there is a strong possibility that small items will be overlooked, leading to errors in the contract documents which in turn can result in numerous changes in the work during construction. The contractor likes the building operation to proceed smoothly with a minimum of changes because a smooth operation is more profitable. Contrary to a widely held belief, contractors do not make money on changes unless they are very substantial.

While tenders which are over budget can cause trouble for the contractor, tenders which are well under budget can be a source of irritation. If a proper cost control program had been put into effect during the pre-tender period, the contractor would have been bidding on a building which more closely resembled the budget, with a consequently larger profit.

When contractors are putting together tenders for stipulated sum contracts they estimate the cost of their own work, then add the lowest bid for each of the sub-trades, the amounts of any cash allowances the architect has included in the specifications, and the company's overheads and profit. The co-ordination required is formidable, particularly since most of the work is now done by sub-contractors who submit their prices by telephone or FAX, many of them in the last few minutes before the tender closes. The owner is likely to receive a lower price and have fewer problems during construction if the confusion is reduced as much as possible, and the architect should bear the following in mind when calling tenders:

1. Whenever possible a selected list of tenderers should be used. A construction project always runs more smoothly when it is being handled by a contractor who has submitted a reasonable price and is trusted by the owner and the consultants. An open list can result in an unknown contractor which may have submitted a low price because of incompetence and which, in attempting to make up its loss, will try to use sub-standard labour and materials, making life difficult for the architect and, if the contractor gets away with it, constructing a building which is inferior to the one the owner expected.

2. Complicated tender forms should be avoided. If numerous unit prices and alternates are essential to a proper analysis of the tender, the low bidder should be asked to submit them within 24 or 48 hours after tendering. The contractor can then give them the consideration they deserve.

3. If addenda are required, the last one should go to the contractor no less than three days before the tender closes. An addendum may appear simple, but for the contractor it may require a considerable revision to the estimate. When the contract documents have been carefully assembled by the architect over a period of some weeks or months, the contractor should at least be given the time to prepare a proper estimate without being inundated with addenda at the last minute.

4. Closing a tender the day after a holiday or a weekend means that the contractors' estimators won't have a holiday or weekend. The best time to close a tender is around the middle of the week, late in the afternoon and preferably when no other tenders are being closed.

All parties to a construction project are affected when there is no pre-tender cost control, either directly as in the case of the building owner, or indirectly as in the case of the consultants, the contractors and their sub-contractors.

CHAPTER 2

Factors Influencing Cost

THE ECONOMY

Construction costs are influenced by factors at three levels. At the highest level is the state of the national economy, whether it is buoyant or depressed and whether or not there is sufficient optimism in the country to invest in capital goods such as construction. At the next level, and greatly influenced by the state of the national economy, is the structure and economic condition of the construction industry itself. The study of economic conditions, both at national level and within the construction industry, really comes within the realm of the economist and the architects can have no control over them, but anyone involved with construction costs should have some knowledge of their effects. Finally there are those factors which affect the cost of the individual building, over which the architects can have some control.

Table 1, based on figures published by Statistics Canada, shows the relationship between the construction industry and other parts of the Canadian economy from 1983 to 1992. In Table 2 the figures have been adjusted for inflation and are shown in constant 1986 dollars. Since each part of the economy experiences different rates of inflation, construction rising at a different rate from fixed capital formation, which covers expenditures by government and industry on machinery and equipment, and both rising at a different rate from (although part of) the gross domestic product, the relationships are different in the two tables, Table 2 being the more meaningful. Table 2 indicates that over this period total construction, including new construction and repairs, represented approximately 13% - 15% of the gross domestic product and about 62% - 72% of fixed capital formation. The construction industry is therefore an important segment of the national economy and any changes in the economy can substantially affect the industry. At the same time, because of the size of the industry, any change in construction activity can have some effect on the economy as a whole.

The demand on the construction industry is largely governed by factors beyond its control because its products are required only if other factors such as interest rates, the availability of mortgages and the demand for goods which factories will produce, are favourable. The social and economic policies of government, both federal and provincial, particularly in the areas of interest rates and taxation, can have a substantial effect. Much of construction is built on borrowed money and an increase in interest rates makes borrowing more expensive. This affects both construction buyers because their capital expenditures increase, and contractors who rely on credit from banks and material suppliers. An increase in taxation reduces profits and purchasing power. A reduction in purchasing power will cause manufacturers to anticipate a lower demand for goods, and to postpone expenditures on new factories and offices. Similarly, service industries such as stores and hotels will put off construction in anticipation of lower sales, and home buyers will have less income available for mortgage payments.

Thus, when money becomes scarce and the future is not being viewed with any optimism by entrepreneurs, there is a tendency for the private sector to reduce capital formation. Since construction forms such a large part of capital formation the volume of construction will drop, tending to lead to a reduction in tender prices as contractors start desperately looking for work and cut profit margins to obtain it. This is inevitably followed by an increase in the number of bankruptcies and a general depression in the construction industry.

On the other hand, a period of excessive inflation will increase the cost of wages and materials, construction costs will rise, and this may also lead to a reduction in the volume of construction because it has become too expensive, particularly if interest rates and land costs have also risen sharply.

The Economic Council of Canada's report *Toward More Stable Growth in Construction* gives an admirable review of instability in the construction industry. On the subject of the construction industry in the economy it states:

Table 1: The Gross Domestic Product, Fixed Capital Formation and Construction Activity in Canada in current dollars

Year	Gross Domestic Product	Fixed Capital Formation	Total Construction Activity	Total Construction Activity as percentage of	
				GDP	FCF
	\$000,000			%	
1983	405,717	81,227	55,948	13.79	68.88
1984	444,735	84,699	56,574	12.72	66.79
1985	477,988	94,198	67,983	14.22	72.17
1986	505,666	101,560	71,701	14.18	70.60
1987	551,597	116,717	81,971	14.86	70.23
1988	605,147	132,958	90,871	15.02	68.35
1989	650,748	146,075	100,412	15.43	68.74
1990	670,952	141,704	102,367	15.26	72.24
1991	675,928	133,529	94,155	13.93	70.51
1992	688,541	129,988	91,861	13.34	70.67

Source: Statistics Canada - Canadian Economic Observer (Catalogue 11-010)
Construction in Canada (Catalogue 64-201)

Table 2: The Gross Domestic Product, Fixed Capital Formation and Construction Activity in Canada in 1986 dollars

Year	Gross Domestic Product	Fixed Capital Formation	Total Construction Activity	Total Construction Activity as percentage of	
				GDP	FCF
	\$000,000			%	
1983	439,448	85,489	61,304	13.95	71.71
1984	467,167	87,395	59,938	12.83	68.58
1985	489,437	95,572	70,066	14.32	73.31
1986	505,666	101,560	71,701	14.18	70.60
1987	526,730	112,505	77,634	14.74	69.00
1988	551,423	124,300	81,614	14.80	65.66
1989	566,486	131,630	85,900	15.16	65.26
1990	565,576	127,140	86,151	15.23	67.76
1991	556,029	124,495	78,535	14.12	63.08
1992	560,048	122,894	75,787	13.53	61.67

Source: Statistics Canada - Canadian Economic Observer (Catalogue 11-010)
Construction in Canada (Catalogue 64-201)

"Construction instability is an integral part of the larger process of economic expansion and contraction locally, regionally and nationally. Since construction firms primarily are marketing highly specialized site-preparation and assembly skills, they carry no inventories. Instead, they respond – as do service agencies – to the immediate demands of other sectors of the economy: to business demands for additional industrial or commercial plant capacity; to government spending on schools, hospitals, energy facilities, roads, sewers and other special structures; and to family requirements for new or replacement housing."

At the same time it points out that while Canada's investment was more stable than the United States in the period 1948-70, "construction in Canada contributed much more to the instability of the economy."

THE CONSTRUCTION INDUSTRY

The structure and current state of the construction industry has an effect on construction costs. The availability and cost of labour and, to a lesser extent, the availability and cost of materials are both within the orbit of the industry and will affect the overall cost of construction, and a shortage of either will cause costs to rise. But the industry also has its own peculiarities which make it quite unlike any other type of manufacturing industry.

The demand on the construction industry can be considered as a demand for investment goods; construction is not done for its own sake but for the goods and services it will help to create. The construction of factories is an investment for production, of roads and highways an investment in infrastructure, of schools and hospitals an investment in social services, and of offices and apartment buildings an investment for income. Even housing might be considered an investment in social enjoyment, although in fact it is more likely to be considered a consumer product rather than an investment. Construction, except for repairs and maintenance, is generally paid for out of capital, either from the entrepreneur's own savings or, more likely, from borrowed capital as are most investments.

The creation of these capital goods by the construction industry is partly a production process, converting raw and semi-finished materials into their final form, and partly an assembly process, assembling manufactured components made elsewhere into a completed product. To do this, production is undertaken on an open site rather than an enclosed factory, and this poses unique problems of organization and management. It also makes production dependent to a certain extent on the weather, and it requires a high degree of mobility of labour and materials. As the Economic Council of Canada put it:

"Teams of construction contractors, tradesmen and other specialists are continually organizing in patterns appropriate to the technical and commercial requirements of each project. When the job is done, they depart to join teams on other projects. This feature of temporary arrangements is characteristic of the construction industry and, in addition to cyclical and seasonal swings in demand, is an important source of insecurity for the participants."

The construction industry is largely sheltered from international competition in the goods it produces. Although the materials it uses may be imported, and some construction materials are exported, the finished product is large, expensive, and remains in a fixed location, unlike the products of most other manufacturing industries. Also, it has a long life compared with other manufactured products. This means that the total stock is large in relation to the annual production, so a small variation in the demand for the total stock will have major repercussions on the industry.

Construction is a widely dispersed and compartmentalized industry, with a wide range of products being produced for its clients by a large number of firms across the country. The products themselves are made specially to the requirements of the client so they are individual in character, requiring their own plans and specifications and containing an immense variety of materials. This means that there are few opportunities for standardization or mass production except in small components. It also means that price determination is a discrete process for each project since no two are identical.

Entry into the construction industry is comparatively easy, particularly at the low end. It does not require a large investment of capital to set up a small construction company and small firms are constantly being formed and dissolved. This helps ensure competition within the industry, as does the ease with which an established firm in one location can open a branch office in another location where profitability might be thought to be higher.

Another unique feature of the construction industry is the unparalleled diffusion of responsibility for the finished product, particularly in the division between design and construction. In most industries the designer and the engineering department work closely in the development of a new product to ensure that their efforts complement each other, but in the construction industry the designer, at least on a stipulated sum contract, does not know who the contractor will be until the design is complete. The designer therefore doesn't know of any special construction techniques which the successful contractor might have developed and which could have been incorporated into the design. This may be overcome to a certain extent by the management contract, but even with this approach there is still a separation between the designer and the subcontractors.

Construction companies are usually expected to submit a price before starting the work. They are expected to include the risks of price fluctuations in their tenders and the building owner, through the use of a construction contract, sets the conditions (although not the price) under which the work will be done. This is the reverse of manufacturing where it is usual for the price to be determined by the manufacturers after the product has been made, at least as a prototype, and its costs known with reasonable certainty. It is the manufacturers who then sets the conditions, subject to competition, under which their products are sold. In other words, in most industries it is the producers who set the terms under which they will do business, and in effect they tell their customers to 'take it or leave it', whereas in construction it is the customer who sets the terms and tells the contractor to 'take it or leave it'.

Tables 3, 4 and 5 give details of some 18,600 construction firms in Canada, of which approximately 11,100 are corporate entities, although it has been estimated that there are in fact probably about 80,000 construction firms, of which approximately 20,000 are corporate entities. Among the incorporated firms, equity financing is proportionately much lower than in the manufacturing or wholesale trades, while short-term debt, especially loans, accounts for a larger share of current liabilities.

THE BUILDING

To this point, all the factors mentioned have been factors external to, and beyond the control of, the architects. At the individual building level, on the other hand, the architects do, to a greater or lesser degree, have some scope to anticipate and control the factors affecting cost. These factors are of various kinds.

Type of Building

The first is the type of building. The kind of building the owner intends to construct will automatically determine a certain magnitude of construction cost. Each building type has its own range of complexities and construction costs and it is impossible, for example, for a hospital to have the same cost per unit of floor area as a parking garage.

Table 3: Characteristics of the Non-Residential Construction Industry in Canada, 1987

Description	Size of Work Undertaken							Total
	$25,000 - $249,000	$250,000 - $499,000	$500,000 - $749,999	$750,000 - $999,000	$1,000,000 - $1,999,999	$2,000,000 - $9,999,999	$10,000,000 and over	
Classification of Firms:								
Type of Company:								
Sole Owner	462	28	14	—	3	2	—	509
Partnership	60	6	3	—	2	4	1	76
Incorporation	703	404	215	158	389	640	203	2,712
Total	1,225	438	232	158	394	646	204	3,297
Principal Type of Construction:								
Industrial	343	102	50	36	79	129	38	777
Commercial	813	283	147	96	253	378	115	2,085
Institutional	69	53	35	26	62	139	51	435
Type of Work:								
New Construction	1,140	424	216	152	383	639	203	3,157
Repairs	85	14	16	6	11	7	1	140
Value of Construction in thousands of dollars:								
Type of Construction:								
Industrial	29,702	33,318	29,787	32,010	107,326	541,751	997,801	1,771,696
Commercial	65,090	89,579	76,637	75,702	312,131	1,415,043	3,382,149	5,416,331
Institutional	8,754	17,149	18,244	19,580	103,555	666,024	1,266,338	2,099,644
Residential	16,550	17,259	12,420	9,446	36,518	125,601	228,506	446,300
Roads and Bridges	10	511	137	558	1,688	14,638	83,413	100,956
Other	442	1,466	2,518	1,119	1,962	35,828	312,433	355,768
Total	120,550	159,282	139,744	138,415	563,180	2,798,885	6,270,640	10,190,695
Type of Work:								
New Construction	108,691	147,200	125,837	128,689	521,356	2,671,971	6,137,766	9,841,510
Repairs	11,859	12,081	13,907	9,726	41,824	126,914	132,874	349,185

Source: Statistics Canada

11

Table 4: Characteristics of the Residential Construction Industry in Canada, 1987

Description	Size of Work Undertaken							Total
	$25,000 - $249,000	$250,000 - $499,000	$500,000 - $749,999	$750,000 - $999,000	$1,000,000 - $1,999,999	$2,000,000 - $9,999,999	$10,000,000 and over	
Classification of Firms:								
Type of Company:								
Sole Owner	5,538	382	70	15	12	2	1	6,020
Partnership	707	149	26	4	14	8	3	911
Incorporation	3,593	1,584	986	514	799	764	139	8,379
Total	9,838	2,115	1,082	533	825	774	143	15,310
Principal Type of Construction:								
Single Family	9,151	2,035	1,024	475	728	634	113	14,160
Row Housing	86	9	13	8	10	18	4	148
Apartments	601	71	45	50	87	122	26	1,002
Type of Work:								
New Construction	9,361	2,021	1,057	509	809	766	143	14,666
Repairs	477	94	25	24	16	8	—	644
Value of Construction in thousands of dollars:								
Type of Construction:								
Single Family	808,729	644,298	562,340	365,570	923,598	2,346,003	2,518,657	8,169,196
Row Housing	10,809	6,313	6,252	8,034	23,143	75,252	140,685	271,388
Apartments	56,012	32,642	35,046	44,072	126,426	531,604	505,901	1,331,702
Non-Residential	73,788	59,417	51,903	40,483	62,860	140,935	131,415	560,801
Roads and Bridges	173	374	395	471	1,200	4,151	69,317	76,081
Other	1,794	2,230	1,999	616	483	2,929	62,092	72,143
Total	951,305	754,273	657,935	460,146	1,137,710	3,100,874	3,428,067	10,481,311
Type of Work:								
New Construction	867,967	700,114	623,390	437,148	1,109,545	3,054,796	3,408,802	10,201,763
Repairs	83,338	45,159	34,545	22,998	28,165	46,078	19,265	279,548

Source: Statistics Canada

Table 5: Characteristics of the Residential and Non-Residential Construction Industry in Canada, 1987

Description	Size of Work Undertaken							
	$25,000 - $249,000	$250,000 - $499,000	$500,000 - $749,999	$750,000 - $999,000	$1,000,000 - $1,999,999	$2,000,000 - $9,999,999	$10,000,000 and over	Total
Classification of Firms:								
Type of Company:								
Sole Owner	6,000	410	84	15	15	4	1	6,529
Partnership	767	155	29	4	16	12	4	987
Incorporation	4,296	1,988	1,201	672	1,188	1,404	342	11,091
Total	11,063	2,553	1,314	691	1,219	1,420	347	18,607
Principal Type of Construction:								
Industrial	343	102	50	36	79	129	38	777
Commercial	813	283	147	96	253	378	115	2,085
Institutional	69	53	35	26	62	139	51	435
Residential	9,838	2,115	1,082	533	825	774	143	15,310
Type of Work:								
New Construction	10,501	2,445	1,273	661	1,192	1,405	346	17,823
Repairs	562	108	41	30	27	15	1	784
Value of Construction in thousands of dollars:								
Type of Construction:								
Industrial	29,702	33,318	29,787	32,010	107,326	541,751	997,801	1,771,696
Commercial	65,090	89,579	76,637	75,702	312,131	1,415,043	3,382,149	5,416,331
Institutional	8,754	17,149	18,244	19,580	103,555	666,024	1,266,338	2,099,644
Non-Residential by Residential Contractors	73,788	59,417	51,903	40,483	62,860	140,935	131,415	560,801
Residential	892,100	700,512	616,059	428,022	1,109,686	3,078,460	3,393,749	10,218,587
Roads and Bridges	184	885	532	1,029	2,888	18,789	152,730	177,037
Other	2,237	3,696	4,516	1,735	2,445	38,757	374,525	427,910
Total	1,071,855	904,555	797,679	598,561	1,700,890	5,899,759	9,698,707	20,672,006
Type of Work:								
New Construction	976,658	847,314	749,227	565,837	1,630,901	5,726,767	9,546,568	20,043,272
Repairs	95,197	57,241	48,452	32,724	69,989	172,992	152,139	628,733

Adapted from Tables 3 & 4

The reason for this is that the type of use and occupancy will determine the general standard of quality of the building systems and finishes, and will govern requirements for ancillary spaces such as the parking space needed for commercial and apartment buildings under the local bylaws. The building type also tends to pre-select the type of contractor who will build it. Non-union (open shop) and residential union contractors and sub-contractors are customarily associated with residential construction, while commercial union contractors and sub-contractors are usually associated with institutional, industrial and commercial buildings. This is not invariably true and some industrial and commercial buildings may be built by residential union or non-union contractors and sub-contractors. There can be a difference in cost (to the building owner) between work performed by these different types of contractor, commercial union contractors usually being the more expensive.

Location

The location of the building can have an influence on the construction cost in a variety of ways. The cost of labour and working conditions will vary from location to location, as will the quality of the labour. Usually the most productive labour is to be found in the major urban areas where, not surprisingly, the labour rates are higher. However, on a unit of production basis variations in productivity and labour costs tend to cancel each other out, so unit prices are not quite so variable as might at first be supposed. A low productivity with a low labour cost gives a unit price which is not dissimilar from a unit price based on high productivity with a high labour cost. On the other hand, labour is more readily available in major urban areas so there is less likelihood of labour shortages and consequent delays.

In major urban areas there are usually enough local contractors, both small and large, to satisfy the demand for construction. A major project which is too big for most of the local contractors would attract large national or regional contractors from outside the area, ensuring that competition is maintained. In less populated areas on the other hand, there are likely to be fewer local contractors able to undertake the work and outside contractors would be less willing to move in, so competition would be more limited.

Ontario and Quebec supply virtually all their own construction materials and are able to export materials to other provinces. It has been estimated that the Atlantic Provinces have to import about 70% of their materials, the Prairies about 50% and British Columbia about 40%. Even within the central provinces there can be some variation. Materials at competitive prices are readily available in the large towns, but are obtained with more difficulty and hence at higher cost in the rural areas, which means local materials should be used whenever possible. In Arctic areas materials become extremely expensive because they have to be imported and transportation costs are high. Great care must be taken in ordering materials in these remote areas because the omission of a few pounds of nails can delay a project until the next shipment of supplies arrives – there is no local hardware store to make good the deficiency.

All municipalities have planning bylaws governing the size and height of buildings, but they vary from municipality to municipality and some are more restrictive than others. Since the size, shape and height of a building will have a direct bearing on its cost, then indirectly the municipal bylaws in effect at the building site will also influence the cost.

When a building is being constructed as a speculative venture its location will determine the type of rents it can command, and this in turn will determine its general quality. A building on a prime site commanding high rents will be of a higher quality and will cost more to build than one on a poor site with low rentals.

A building on a downtown site in a large city may have very restricted access, requiring traffic control when materials are being delivered, or requiring that materials can only be delivered at certain times of the day. There may also be difficulties in storing materials on the site because of space limitations. All these restrictions will add to the cost. On suburban or country sites there are usually no problems of access or storage, although access can be a major problem in Arctic areas. In the Arctic, access may only be feasible at certain times of the year and facilities such as roads, boat docks or aircraft landing strips may have to be provided to make it possible at all. Also, the restricted access may make it necessary to build canteen, recreation and health facilities as well as sleeping accommodation for the workers. It is not unknown for the cost of these temporary facilities to equal or exceed the cost of the building being constructed.

The location of the site will determine its cost, sites in major urban centres costing rather more than sites in rural areas. This in turn will govern the type and quality of the building which is constructed, and possibly its size, shape and height.

The Site

Closely allied to the location of the site is the site itself. A building which is to be erected on a confined site with other buildings adjoining it, and possibly with a major street running beside it, will probably need to have shoring to the excavation, and some, if not all, of the adjacent buildings may need to be underpinned. This is a problem which can easily be overlooked when preparing a preliminary estimate on a project. A confined site can influence the shape and height of the building, while a large site puts no such restrictions on the building unless it is an undulating site, in which case the form of the building should take advantage of the contours.

The type of soil conditions found at the site will influence the design of the foundations, will determine whether special costs such as sheet piling or pumping will be required, and will generally affect the cost of excavation and other foundation work. In particular, the disposal of contaminated soil, sometimes found in major urban areas, can be a major element of cost. Despite this, it is not unknown for some owners to buy a poor site knowing that, although the site may be relatively inexpensive, the construction cost will be higher. They will have calculated that the saving in the purchase price of the site more than offsets the premium in construction cost caused by the poor soil conditions.

Shape

The shape of the building can have a major effect on the construction cost. Figure 1 shows the plan of several buildings of various shapes and sizes, and Table 6 shows the data associated with them. All buildings are assumed to be single-storey, with a storey height of 10 units. Buildings A to E all have the same gross floor area , although they are of different shapes, and Building F is larger than the others.

Building	Area	Perimeter	Cladding Area	Cladding Ratio	Cladding Cost	Cost per unit^2
A	10,000	400	4,000	0.40	$400,000	$40.00
B	10,000	500	5,000	0.50	$500,000	$50.00
C	10,000	600	6,000	0.60	$600,000	$60.00
D	10,000	520	5,200	0.52	$520,000	$42.00
E	10,000	560	5,600	0.56	$560,000	$56.00
F	250,000	2,000	20,000	0.08	$2,000,000	$8.00

Table 6

While Building A is square, Building B is rectangular, and this change in shape gives Building B a longer perimeter than Building A. With exterior cladding ten units high in both cases, this will result in a cladding

CONSTRUCTION BUDGETING

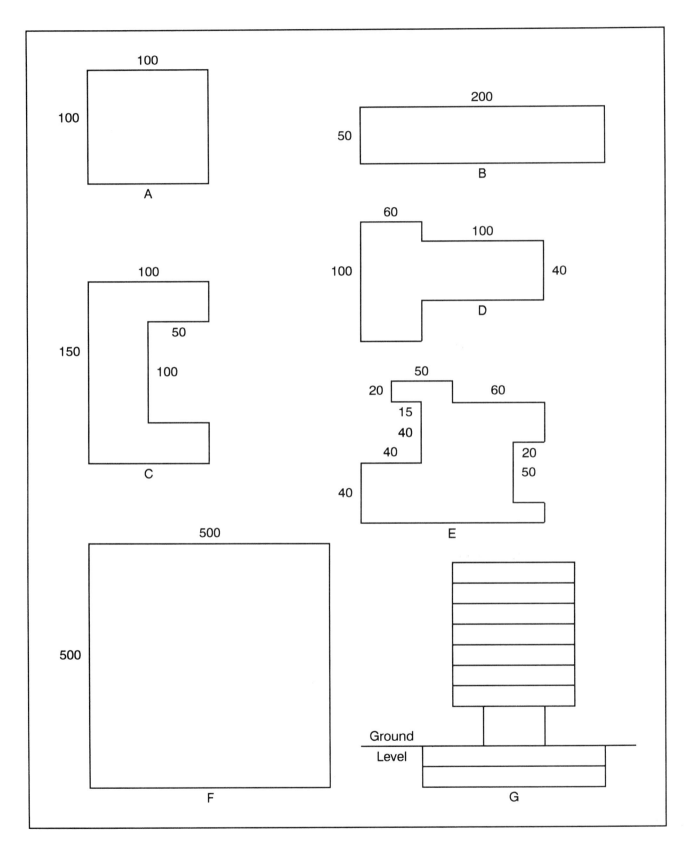

Figure 1

area of 4,000 square units for Building A and 5,000 square units for Building B. At a cost of $100.00 per square unit for cladding, Building B will have a cladding cost of $500,000 making it $100,000 more than Building A. The final column in Table 6 shows the cost of the cladding in each building as a cost per square unit of the gross floor area. The change in shape has increased the cost of Building B by $10.00 per square unit.

Compared to the simple square shape of Building A, Buildings C, D and E all have shapes which have increased the perimeter, and hence the cost, to varying degrees. It is generally true to say that any variation from the square, other than to a circle, will increase the cost of cladding because the ratio of exterior wall to enclosed space is increased. These examples show the effect on the cladding cost, but the cost of air conditioning and heating will also be increased because of the increased cladding ratio. It is also worth noting that exterior corner columns, being eccentrically loaded, are more costly than interior columns, and this will also add to the costs of Buildings C, D and E.

The most efficient shape in terms of the ratio between its perimeter and its area is the circle, but circular buildings, while not unknown, are usually more expensive to set out and to build, and also give the designer problems in planning the interior.

Size

Size has a significant effect on the cladding cost as can be seen by Building F in Table 6. Like Building A, this building is square but its sides are five times longer, which results in a ratio of cladding area to floor area of only 0.08 and a saving of $32.00 in the cost per square unit of the gross floor area. It is generally true that as the floor plan of a building increases, the cost per square unit of the gross floor area attributable to perimeter cladding will reduce. This means that it is normally less expensive to incorporate a given amount of floor space in one large building than to spread it out over a number of smaller buildings.

The size of a project can also have an influence on the type of contractor who can build it. Small and medium-sized construction companies tend to build projects commensurate with their size and to operate within their own geographical area, so for small and medium-sized projects competition is likely to be between a large number of local contractors. For larger projects the number of interested local contractors would be reduced, but this would be partly offset by larger contractors from a wider area being interested. The size of the project is therefore not likely to materially reduce the amount of competition unless it is particularly large or complicated, making it of interest only to the largest and most sophisticated contractors.

Height

It is less easy to generalize about the effect of height on cost than it is to generalize about the shape and size. The height of a building is often governed by the site and the local planning by-laws, but for a given floor area it is generally, but not invariably, true to say that a single-storey building will cost more than a two storey building. This is because the single-storey building has twice the area of foundations, slab on grade and roof finish, while the area of roof construction is equal to the combined areas of floor and roof construction in the two-storey building. Even the improved cladding ratio for the single-storey building because of the increased size of the building's footprint and the need for stairs in a two-storey building, does not usually offset these premiums. This will not apply when floor loadings are large, necessitating an extra heavy construction for the upper floor in the two-storey building, or where the roof construction of the single-storey building can be comparatively light, making its unit cost considerably less than a suspended floor. Both these conditions usually prevail in factory and warehouse buildings and this, combined with the ease of material handling in a single-storey as compared with a multi-storey building, is why these types of building are normally single-storey structures.

Above two storeys each additional floor adds to the cost for a given floor area. Additional floors reduce the plan size making the cladding ratio less efficient. More elevators have to be introduced as the building becomes higher, adding to the cost of construction and reducing the ratio of net to gross floor area. Besides these considerations, electrical and mechanical systems become more complicated, the structure of the lower floors has to be designed to carry the upper floors, the building has to be able to withstand wind and seismic loadings, and construction costs will tend to increase because of the extra cost of hoisting equipment and the extra time needed to get men and materials to their locations in multi-storey buildings.

The other aspect of height – the storey height of each floor – is usually determined by the building owner's requirements and the dictates of the structural and mechanical designs. Any increase in storey height will, of course, directly affect the ratio between the area of cladding and the gross floor area and increase the capital and operating costs.

Projections

The shape of the building on section can also have an effect on the construction cost. Projecting or recessed balconies require additional expense for their construction and finish, and recessed balconies will change the shape of the building and increase its cladding ratio.

Buildings which have a ground, or any, floor which is smaller than the floors above it, such as Building G in Figure 1, will have additional costs. The exposed soffit of the projecting second floor where it is exposed has to be insulated and finished, the roof over the basement extending beyond the ground floor has to be waterproofed and paved whereas normally it would form part of the ground floor, and the columns supporting the perimeter of the second floor will probably require special treatment. The net effect of this design is to reduce the total floor area while at the same time increasing the total cost.

Exterior Cladding

A change in the size, shape or height of a building can change the quantity of exterior cladding and its relationship to the gross floor area, and this in turn will have an effect on the building's cost. Size, shape and height are usually decided in the early stages of design, so exterior cladding is one of the earliest building elements which can be manipulated by the design team to adjust cost. Once the size, shape and height have been settled, a major cost decision has been made, although further adjustments can take place when materials for the exterior cladding are being selected.

In comparison with interior partitions, exterior cladding is expensive because it needs to be weatherproofed and insulated, and it only encloses space on one side. It is therefore preferable whenever possible, and subject to planning efficiency mentioned below, to attempt to reduce the quantity of exterior cladding, even if this means increasing the quantity of interior partitions.

In addition to the cost of the cladding itself, the exterior cladding is where heat losses and heat gains are made, so the quantity of cladding, including the roof, has a great effect on both the capital and the running costs of the heating and cooling systems.

Planning Efficiency

Before the final shape and height of a building is settled a careful look at the planning of the interior is needed. A building which has an efficient shape in terms of the ratio of exterior cladding to enclosed space may require an increased amount of circulation area, or make it difficult to incorporate storage or mechanical spaces within it. A saving of five per cent in the cost per unit of floor area because of a good cladding ratio is wasted if it has caused the building to be enlarged to a gross floor area which is ten per cent more than it needs to be. The question of net to gross floor areas should always be studied at an early stage in the design process since it is not unknown for a building to appear to be economical on the basis of its cost per unit of floor area, while in fact it is larger than the building owner really needs.

Planning efficiency can also be affected by the structural bay sizes. Smaller bay sizes will reduce structural costs but the increased number of columns makes it more difficult for the architects to plan the spaces around them efficiently.

Materials

Considerations of size, shape and height relate to decisions which are made in the early stages of design and once these decisions have been made the cost implications have largely been settled. It then remains for decisions to be made as to the type and quality of materials and systems which, while important, do not have the same profound cost effects.

The prime requirement for economy when it comes to working details is simplicity. Uncomplicated, clear and unambiguous drawings and specifications not only help reduce costs on the site but also ensure that truly competitive tenders are received. Contractors whose estimators don't really understand the drawings or specifications may cover themselves with an inflated price, but are more likely to be in a position to claim large extras during construction. In either case the building owner will be paying extra for the architects' obscurity.

Allied to simplicity is the designer's need to recognize the stock sizes of materials so that they can be incorporated into the building with a minimum amount of wastage, and to use standard manufactured components rather than custom-made products. Using expensive materials where less expensive materials would be quite adequate not only increases the cost of materials unnecessarily but also tends to increase the cost of labour. A walnut door, for example, takes more time and trouble to hang just because it is an expensive door than does a simple hollow-core birch door.

Finally, formwork is the most expensive single element in concrete construction. When the costs of a reinforced concrete building are analyzed it is usually found that the formwork costs far exceed the cost of the concrete or reinforcing steel. This is the reason for some structural designers maintaining the same size of columns all the way up the building, making the necessary adjustments in the amount of reinforcing steel, in order that the column forms can be re-used without having to be re-worked on each floor. In fact any saving in formwork, such as the use of flying forms, will help reduce the costs of concrete construction.

Type of Contract

The most common form of construction contract is the stipulated sum contract, in which all the contract documents are prepared in advance of construction. The contract documents consist of working drawings and specifications describing the scope of the work together with any addenda which may be issued prior to tender closing, used initially by the general contractors bidding the project to prepare lump sum tenders, and then accompanied by a standard form of contract published jointly by the Royal Architectural Institute of Canada and the Canadian Construction Association which forms the basis of the agreement between the client and the successful contractor. This type of contract has several advantages. It is well understood so, provided the scope of the work has been clearly defined, there should be few opportunities for misunderstanding between the parties. The architects and their engineers have time to review the design and ensure that it is complete before the contractor is selected and construction starts. It allows for competition among several contractors so, in theory at least, the building owner pays the lowest possible price. Once tenders have been received the owner knows, subject to changes which may occur during construction, what the cost of the building will be before becoming finally committed to it. It also has some disadvantages. The design team completes its design before the contractor has been appointed, so the contractor is not available to give advice on, for example, innovative or more economical construction techniques. It can take some time to prepare complete working drawings and specifications, and some owners would prefer to reduce this time and have earlier occupancy of the building. Finally, only the contractor knows how the price was established, and a lump sum tender gives the architects very little useful cost information for future projects.

A stipulated sum contract may also be phased, the foundation work for example being awarded as one contract, followed by another tender call for the superstructure when the foundations have been completed. Phasing the construction in this way has the advantage that the total time can be reduced since the design of the superstructure can be completed while the foundations are being built. Phasing is sometimes used when construction is being partially financed by public contributions, such as a hospital, where the client wishes to show the local community as soon as possible that their funds are being put to good use. A disadvantage of phased construction is that if tenders on the second contract are too high the client can be faced with a partially completed building and insufficient funds to complete it. Usually the contractor who obtained the first contract will be allowed to tender on the second. If this contractor is successful on the second contract there should be no problem. But if it is awarded to another contractor there is a possibility of disputes, which the building owner and the consultants will have to settle, if the second contractor asks for extras to correct errors claimed to have been found in the first contractor's work.

Another familiar form of contract is the cost plus contract in which the contractor agrees to build at cost, plus a mark-up for overhead and profit, usually stated as a lump sum or as a percentage of the cost. The only advantage of this method is that it enables the contractor to start work on the site sooner than would have been possible under a stipulated sum contract since it is not necessary to wait until all the drawings and specifications have been completed. It might also be used for a complicated renovation project where it is impossible to estimate the cost in advance. Its disadvantages are numerous. The total cost is unknown until the work is finished and the final bill presented to the building owner. When the mark-up is based on a percentage of the cost the contractor has a positive incentive to increase the costs and to put the least experienced supervisors and workers on the job. And there is often very little competition, particularly on smaller projects when a single sub-contractor may be asked to submit a price on a specialized part of work with no other sub-contractor being asked to give a competitive quotation. In comparison with a stipulated sum contract, therefore, the cost to the building owner is most likely to be more if a cost plus contract is used.

A variation is a cost plus contract with a maximum upset price. This at least ensures that the building owner knows what the maximum cost will be since it should not exceed the maximum price, but the other disadvantages of the cost plus contract remain, and wise contractors will make sure the maximum upset price is sufficiently high that it will not cause them problems. A further variation is to include a participation clause which allows the building owner and the contractor to share proportionally in any savings between the actual final cost and the maximum upset price. This gives the contractor some incentive to reduce costs, but only below what might already be an inflated maximum upset price. It is generally agreed that an increase in the scope of work requires an increase in the maximum upset price, but problems can be encountered in agreeing upon what constitutes a saving in which both parties participate. For example, should the contractor participate in a saving which was suggested by the owner? This type of contract, like the ordinary cost plus contract, is likely to be more expensive to the building owner than a stipulated sum contract.

A management contract, also known as fast-track, is not unlike a cost plus contract although there are some crucial differences. A construction manager, who may be an individual, a construction management firm or a construction company is appointed to manage the construction. The appointment may be made by selecting a firm or an individual in whom the building owner and the architects have confidence and with whom the owner can negotiate a fee, or by competitive tender among a group of firms or individuals. If the latter method is used it should be remembered that the essence of a management contract is good construction management. This is not always provided, and quite possibly will not be provided, by an individual or a firm submitting the lowest fee. The construction manager is expected to work with the design team during the development of working drawings and specifications, and to follow this up by managing the work of construction on the site much as a general contractor would on a stipulated sum contract. The drawings and specifications are prepared in sequence in trade packages, and tenders are called from the sub-trades as they are required to meet the construction schedule. The architects will, for example, concentrate on the roofing drawings and specifications when roofing is the next trade package required in the construction sequence, and will postpone consideration of interior finishes until they are the next in sequence. Instead of entering into one contract with a general contractor the owner enters into multiple contracts, starting with the construction manager and ending with the final trade contract.

The advantages of a management contract are that, like a cost plus contract, work can start on the site with very little delay, before all the drawings and specifications have been finalized. Because the management contractor is not required to do any of the construction work, other than minor work which cannot be sub-let, all prices are competitive since the sub-trade packages are all called by competitive tender and the building owner enters into separate contracts with each sub-trade. This means that the owner and the consultants are privy to all the costs which make up the total cost of the building. Another, sometimes illusory, advantage is that the management contractor is available to give practical advice to the design team. The contractor cannot usually be brought in at the very beginning of the project because some knowledge of the type, size and standard of quality of the building is needed before the contractor can quote a fee, but the contractor's input can be invaluable when it comes to practical construction details.

The main disadvantage of this type of contract is that the building owner doesn't know what the total cost commitment will be until the last tender has been called and, as with phased construction mentioned earlier, it is possible for the owner to run out of money part way through construction if the early trade packages exceed the budget by substantial amounts. The actual construction cost to the owner is likely to be the same as it would be with a stipulated sum contract, the principal saving being in the earlier occupancy of the building, but the costs to the design team are likely to be greater since they are put to considerably more work.

A design-build or turnkey contract puts the responsibility for both the design and the construction of a project into the hands of the contractor. Tenders are called for proposals to design and build the project and it is then up to the building owner to analyze the proposals and determine which provides the best building at the best price. A tender call of this type requires a clear and unambiguous description of the owner's requirements and, when tenders have been received, a careful evaluation of the proposals to ensure that they are complete, both of which should be done by consultants engaged by the building owner.

The Architect

The architects and their engineers can have an effect on construction costs. Some consultants have a reputation for being expensive, based not only on the way in which they design their buildings, but also on the quality of their drawings and specifications and their attitude toward the contractor and the sub-contractors during construction.

As noted earlier, unclear or ambiguous drawings and specifications may force contractors to include a contingency in their tenders to protect themselves, but they are also likely to give rise to successful claims for extras during construction.

Contractors soon learn which architects and engineers are likely to be unreasonable in their demands during construction, or who will delay them by not producing the information they need, and will add a premium to their tenders to cover the anticipated additional costs.

CHAPTER 3

Estimating Methods

THE CONTRACTOR'S METHOD

When contractors and sub-contractors submit tenders they first have to make a detailed breakdown of all the quantities of labour and materials which will be required for the project, each of which has to be priced to enable them to estimate the total cost. This is usually referred to as the quantity survey method. At this stage, it should be remembered, it is only an estimate of the total cost. Only when the building is finished does the contractor know the true cost and whether or not the company has made a profit, although a prudent contractor will keep track of the actual costs and compare them with the estimate throughout the construction period.

The measurement of quantities, the first stage in the process, is a technical function requiring a good knowledge of construction and an ability to visualize the work as it will be built. Since there are a number of ways in which the quantities can be measured and presented for pricing, the Canadian Institute of Quantity Surveyors has published the *Method of Measurement of Construction Works* which sets out the general rules to be followed to provide a degree of standardization in the measurement and presentation of the quantities. Many contractors in Canada follow this document and it is used as a basis for teaching the measurement of quantities in most, if not all, technical colleges.

The second stage in the process, the application of unit prices, requires the same skills as those needed for measuring the quantities, together with experience and a detailed knowledge of site operations, which is why pricing is usually done by the contractor's chief estimator.

There are three basic elements of a unit price: labour, material and equipment. Labour is undoubtedly the most difficult to estimate, requiring a detailed knowledge of the time required to perform all the various activities on the site and an understanding of what factors can affect them. Most contractors have some form of reporting system from the site to the head office. In its simplest form it may only be a weekly report of the total cost for payroll purposes. Without any breakdown or explanation of the work which was being performed, this information is not of much help to the estimator.

A more useful form of report would give a breakdown, either in man-hours or in labour cost, of each of the operations being performed on the site. This enables the contractor's estimating department to compare the actual costs with the estimated costs and to record the information for future estimates. Care has to be taken in analyzing this data because a busy site staff can unintentionally distort reports, while an unscrupulous superintendent can distort reports deliberately to cover up errors.

If the report is based on the labour costs rather than on man-hours, the estimating department would find it useful to analyze the costs back into man-hours to give labour constants or man-hour factors. A labour constant is a representation of the number of man-hours required to perform a given operation. If it is known, for example, that on average a carpenter can hang ten hollow core, birch-faced flush doors of a given size in an eight-hour day, then it requires 0.8 hours of his (or her) time for each door, and this is the labour constant for hanging this type of door. If one labourer is needed to help each pair of carpenters, then the labour constant for the labourer would be 0.4 hours. These times, multiplied by the appropriate labour rates, will give the total cost of hanging a door, as follows:

0.8	hours carpenter	@ $32.00	=	$25.60
0.4	hours labourer	@ $28.00	=	11.20
Total				$36.80

While these labour constants may have been obtained from one project, the next project may show a different set of constants and it is up to the estimator to find out, if possible, why they differ. Once the differing conditions which occurred for the same operation on two different projects have been discovered, the estimator is in a better position to allow for them on future estimates.

An alternative to the labour constant method of estimating costs, and one which is perhaps a little more practical, is the crew cost method. It also requires feedback from the site, but instead of analyzing the information into labour constants it is analyzed to show the production which might be expected from a crew of workers in a day. Using the same example of hanging a door, the crew might consist of two carpenters and a labourer, and their production might be twenty doors in an eight-hour day. The cost of this crew for one day will be:

2 carpenters x 8 hours	=	16 hours @ $32.00 =	$512.00
1 labourer x 8 hours	=	8 hours @ $28.00 =	224.00
			_____
Total			$736.00
			======

With a production of twenty doors per day the unit cost per door will be $736 divided by 20, or $36.80, the same as in the last example.

This method has certain advantages over the labour constant method. It is easier for the site staff, if they have occasion to review the estimate, to visualize a crew producing a certain volume of work in a day than it is for them to visualize the rather abstract labour constants. For the same reason it is easier for the estimator to adjust for site conditions and to make allowances for changes in productivity when pricing the estimate. Also the estimate can more easily be used as a means for determining site labour requirements when the contractor is scheduling the job.

It should be noted that the labour rates used in the calculations above are the hourly rates to be paid by the contractor and not the hourly rates paid to the workers. Such extras as vacation pay, workers' compensation, union check offs and other fringe benefits that are paid by the employer over and above the worker's hourly rate have to be included in the estimate. These can be added to the hourly rate as has been done here, or they can be carried as a percentage on the total cost of labour at the end of the estimate as is done by some contractors. However it is done, these extras have to be included in the estimate, otherwise their cost will come out of the contractor's anticipated profit.

Material is easier to estimate than labour because it is usually just a matter of obtaining quotations from suppliers. But the contractor's estimator must check whether the quoted price includes the cost of delivery to the site or whether this has to be added to the price, whether discounts are available, whether sales taxes have been included, and the amount of duty which has to be paid on imported materials.

A major problem with estimating some material costs is determining what allowance should be made for waste. The *Method of Measurement of Construction Works* states that all measurements shall be made net, which means that the unit prices have to allow for all the wasted materials. Many materials have waste associated with them: plywood panelling which is bought in 1200mm x 2400mm (4'0" x 8'0") sheets will have at least one-eighth wasted if it is to be installed on walls which are 2100mm (7'0") high, and wood framing always has to be cut to correct lengths with a consequent waste of material. It is highly likely that some materials will be stolen, and all the bricks, blocks and mortar which have been purchased don't finish up in the building. Waste is usually allowed for as a percentage addition to the material cost, the actual amount varying from material to material, but the extent of wastage will also depend on the design of the building and on the calibre of the workers. If the architects have not recognized the standard dimensions of some of the materials in the design more will be wasted, and if inefficient workers waste more materials than was allowed for in the estimate, the contractor's costs will be higher than had been anticipated.

If the *Method of Measurement of Construction Works* is not being used as a guideline, the allowance for waste can be incorporated in the measurement by adding the appropriate percentage to the quantities, in which case no allowance need be made to the unit prices. It is important that the estimator is clear about which convention is being followed otherwise wastage might be added to both the quantity and the unit price.

The cost of equipment can either be included as part of the unit price, or it can be added at the end of the estimate as one of the items of site overhead. The cost of vibrators for concrete, for example, is usually included as part of the cost of placing the concrete, while the cost of a crane used for hoisting the concrete into place is usually included in the site overhead because it is also used for hoisting other materials. The cost of the equipment is calculated on the time it will be required on the job. Added to this will be the cost of transporting it to and from the site, erecting and dismantling it, the cost of labour operating it and the fuel and other supplies needed to run it. Some equipment is rented, but even if it is owned by the contractor it will be charged to the job at current rental rates to cover the contractor's ownership costs.

When the contractor has estimated the direct cost of labour, materials and equipment for the work which will be done by its own forces, the cost of work which will be sub-contracted is added, together with any cash allowances which have been included in the specification, the cost of site overheads, and the contractor's head office overhead and profit. Site overheads, besides major equipment which has already been mentioned, will include supervision, insurance, bonds, hoarding, site offices and sheds, permits and so on. A summary of items usually included as site overheads is given in *Elemental Cost Analysis – Method of Measurement and Pricing* published by the Canadian Institute of Quantity Surveyors. Head office overhead and profit, unlike the rest of the estimate which can be estimated directly, is calculated as a percentage of the total cost or is included as a lump sum. It is intended to cover the cost of the contractor's head office including staff, rent, heating, lighting and supplies etc. plus an allowance for profit.

For a more detailed description of the contractor's method of estimating reference should be made to *Bidding and Estimating Procedures for Construction* by G.L. Mansfield, published by Reston Publishing Company, Inc. This book is a very readable and practical guide to estimating and bidding for contractors.

A contractor's estimator, if the contracting firm is at all efficient, will have most of this detailed cost information readily available. For those who are not working in a contractor's office the following publications may be of some help in obtaining cost information:

Means Construction Cost Data published annually by Robert Snow Means Company, Inc., 100 Construction Plaza, P.O. Box 800, Kingston, MA 02364-0800.
This is a compendium of unit prices based on average costs throughout the United States. It is very comprehensive and can be useful when other sources are not readily available. In addition to the unit prices, it gives the daily output for a number of different crews so that labour costs can be calculated using local labour rates, and has an index to adjust the rates for several Canadian cities.

Construction Pricing and Scheduling Manual published annually by McGraw-Hill Information Systems Company, 330 West 42 Street, New York, N.Y. 10035.
This publication is similar to Means.

Yardsticks for Costing published annually by Southam Business Publications Limited, 1450 Don Mills Road, Don Mills, Ontario.
This publication has fewer prices than Means or McGraw-Hill, but it contains unit prices for seven cities in Canada and has a quarterly updating service.

Boeckh Building Valuation Manual (3 volumes) published by American Appraisal Canada Inc., Publication and Education Division, 310 Front Street West, Toronto.

These books give costs for a large variety of buildings together with unit prices for a number of different materials, and are supplemented by a bimonthly publication giving updating factors for the costs. They are intended primarily for building appraisers.

The Building Estimator's Reference Book published by Frank R. Walker Company in Chicago.

This book, which can be bought at any good technical bookshop, does not contain unit prices but it does have labour constants and other estimating data which can be useful in establishing unit prices.

The first four of these publications can be quite useful, but should be used with some discretion since they contain average prices which may not apply specifically to any one particular project. They can therefore be of use to architects, engineers or quantity surveyors who are trying to establish a budget, or who are making a comparison between different types of construction or finishes, but they are unlikely to be used by a contractor who is submitting a tender.

Other ways of obtaining cost information for those not employed with construction companies include personal observation on the site, negotiating the cost of changes with contractors, and talking to contractors, sub-contractors or suppliers to learn current unit prices. This last has to be done warily, particularly in the case of specialist sub-contractors and suppliers. Some tend to quote high figures so that there will be no recrimination afterwards, while others tend to quote low figures in the hope that it will ensure that their product is specified. A careful assessment must be made to verify the accuracy of the figures.

THE DESIGN CONSULTANTS' METHODS

The only way contractors or sub-contractors can prepare their estimates with any assurance of accuracy is to make a detailed analysis of all the labour, material and equipment which will be required for the job, with a trade-by-trade breakdown of the costs. This method is not usually appropriate for architects or consulting quantity surveyors for the following reasons:

1. Contractors' estimates are calculated from detailed drawings and specifications. Architects or quantity surveyors, particularly in the early design stages, have less information on which to base their estimates and couldn't measure detailed quantities even if they wanted to.

2. Contractors know that if they are low bidder they will be awarded the contract and be able to start construction shortly after completing their estimate, provided there are no unforeseen delays, and because it is based on completed working drawings and specifications they can assess the duration of the project with reasonable accuracy. Architects or quantity surveyors on the other hand may be preparing a preliminary estimate on a project which will not start construction until some months or years in the future, the duration of which will be more difficult to gauge because of a lack of design information. They are therefore trying to project costs much further into the future than the contractors. Although they may include an allowance to cover cost escalation, the measurement of detailed quantities, even if this were possible, with what may well turn out to be inaccurate unit prices would be pointless.

3. Contractors have estimating departments and a substantial amount of detailed cost information flowing in from the site, together with firm price quotations from sub-contractors and suppliers. Most architects do not have an estimating department and very often the only detailed cost information they

25

have is trade breakdowns from previous projects. Such breakdowns are likely to be misleading because they were provided by the contractors for progress payment purposes, not to help architects with their estimates, and will most likely be distorted by having money transferred from the later trades into the early trades in order to help the contractor finance the project. Without an estimating department and with inadequate or misleading cost information the average architect is not able to make an estimate in the same amount of detail as a contractor.

4. Contractors prepare their estimates with the object of obtaining work. They have no wish to lose money on their projects so their estimates have to be as accurate as is humanly possible. Pre-tender estimates by architects or quantity surveyors are provided to advise building owners of their probable financial commitment, and to help control costs during the design stage, and do not therefore need to have quite the same degree of accuracy. Since the objectives are different, the estimating method should also be different.

5. Contractors need to break their costs down into a trade format because this is how their own cost information is organized and how they receive the sub-trade prices. As will be explained later, a trade breakdown is of little help to architects or quantity surveyors in controlling costs in the pre-tender period.

6. The contractor's method of estimating is very accurate but extremely time consuming. Architects or quantity surveyors who may have to prepare several estimates on alternative design solutions in the early stages of a project need a method which is, perhaps, rather less accurate but much quicker.

Accepting the fact that the contractor's method of estimating is not generally suited to a pre-tender estimate, any alternative which might be suitable should be looked at with three requirements in mind. First, it should be reasonably accurate, since there is obviously no point in using a method which consistently produces inaccurate results. Second, it should be reasonably fast, because it may be used for making decisions on alternative design solutions, and these decisions usually have to be made quickly. Third, it should provide a means of controlling as well as estimating the cost. The first two requirements are always in conflict with each other. A fast estimate is frequently not very accurate, and an accurate estimate usually requires time for its preparation, but a reasonable balance must be reached between the two.

All estimating methods can be classified as either single-rate or multiple-rate methods. Traditionally, architects have tended toward single-rate methods because of their simplicity and ease of use.

Single-rate Methods

A single-rate method, as its name implies, is an estimate in which a single quantity is multiplied by a single unit price to arrive at a total estimated cost. The most common single-rate methods are the unit cost and the square metre or square foot methods.

Unit Cost Method

In the unit cost method the cost is analyzed as a cost per unit of accommodation. Examples would be the cost per car in a parking garage, the cost per student in a school, the cost per bed in a hospital and the cost per suite in an apartment building. The cost is analyzed by the simple process of dividing the known cost of a building by the appropriate unit of accommodation. An estimate is made just as simply by multiplying the calculated number of units in a proposed building by the previously analyzed cost per unit.

This method is very fast but not very accurate because it is difficult to make adjustments to the unit cost for changes in size, shape, quality or type of construction. Nor is it useful in controlling costs because it gives no information about what is included in the unit cost.

While it is not recommended as an estimating method, it can be used by a school board or a hospital commission for establishing overall construction budgets. If, for example, a school board estimates that it will have to provide for an additional 1,550 students over the next few years it can calculate its budget by multiplying 1,550 by an average estimated cost per pupil place. The unit cost method can also be used as a quick check to ensure that an estimate arrived at by another method looks reasonable. Finally, it can be used as a yardstick to compare the known costs of one building with another of the same type.

Square Metre Method

The square metre method (formerly the square foot method) is probably the most common method used by architects, and it is certainly the most common way of discussing building costs. It is also the method which has resulted in many inaccurate preliminary estimates.

The principal advantage of this method is that the gross floor area is related to usable space and is therefore readily understood by the building owner and, in theory at least, it should be reasonably accurate because a major part of the cost of a building is contained in, or related to, its horizontal components. Like the unit cost method, analysis is done by the division of a known construction cost by the appropriate unit, in this case the gross floor area, and an estimate is made by multiplying the gross floor area of a proposed building by the previously analyzed cost per square metre or per square foot.

Because of its common use as both an estimating method and as a means of comparing construction costs, it is important that the terms used in this method are accurately defined. The Canadian Institute of Quantity Surveyors' booklet *Measurement of Buildings by Area and Volume* gives a set of rules for the measurement of the gross floor area which is now generally accepted. At the same time, the cost should also be defined, although there is not yet any generally accepted way of doing so. The cost is always recognized as the cost which the contractor charges the building owner for a building, not the cost to the contractor for building it. However, the cost of one building may, for example, include the furnishings and site works, while another excludes them. A discussion of square metre or square foot costs in which the parties each have a different interpretation of the meaning of the total cost of the building, even though they have both measured their buildings in the same way, becomes meaningless.

This method, while not as fast as the unit cost method, is faster than most other methods but it is not particularly accurate because, like the unit cost method, it is not easy to make adjustments to the unit price for changes in size, shape, quality or type of construction. It is also not helpful in controlling costs. Its main uses might be in checking results determined by some other estimating method, and in comparing the costs of two similar buildings.

Cubic Foot Method

Before metrification, when buildings were measured in feet and inches, the cubic foot method was frequently used, and at one time was considered to be superior to the square foot method. It was a variation of the square foot method, the measurement going one step further and incorporating the height as well as the area to give a building volume. It is never used now, except for a preliminary estimate of demolition, because it has two major defects. The first is that, while it takes the third dimension into account, in doing so it tends to produce misleading information. The measurement of the volume of a building doesn't give any indication of what is contained within that volume. A cubic foot cost may be high either because the designer has been able to incorporate more usable space into the building, perhaps by reducing the storey heights in order to introduce an additional floor into the same volume, or because more expensive materials or construction details have been used. It was therefore difficult to judge why two buildings had different cubic foot costs – the reason one was higher than the other may have been because the designer was either more efficient or more expensive, and it is not immediately apparent which.

The other major defect of this method was that a large volume was multiplied by a small unit price, and a small variation in the unit price would result in a large variation in the total cost. This was particularly true when imperial measurements were used and millions of cubic feet had to be multiplied by a few cents per cubic foot.

The cubic foot method also had the same drawbacks as the square foot method and these, combined with its two major defects, do not recommend it as a method of estimating cost.

The one advantage of any single-rate method is that the unit rate incorporates all the costs to be found in the building so there is no danger of leaving anything out. Against this is the bigger disadvantage that with only one quantity to price, an error in the unit rate will mean that the entire estimate is wrong. A single-rate method requires someone with a great deal of experience if the estimate is to be tolerably accurate, and even then accuracy is more likely to be the result of good luck rather than good judgement.

Multiple-rate Methods

Multiple-rate methods require the measurement of more than one quantity, and consequently the use of more than one unit rate and a form of breakdown. Because the estimate contains more detail there is always the possibility of inadvertently omitting some items of work, but against this an error in any of the unit rates does not necessarily invalidate the whole estimate, particularly since the law of compensating errors is likely to come into effect. Multiple-rate methods take longer to calculate than single-rate methods but are generally more accurate and they can be used as an aid in controlling costs. The most familiar multiple-rate method is the quantity survey method used by contractors which was described in the opening section of this chapter.

Unit In Place Method

The unit in place method, not to be confused with the unit cost method, and sometimes known as the approximate quantities method, is a simplified form of the quantity survey method used by contractors. With the quantity survey method, for example, a reinforced concrete wall would be estimated by measuring the volume of concrete, the area of formwork and the mass of reinforcing steel, each listed and priced separately and possibly with separate costs for labour, material and equipment. In contrast, for the unit in place method the area of the wall would be measured and a single overall unit price used to cover the combined costs of labour, material and equipment for the concrete, formwork and reinforcing steel. Such a unit price for a project designed in metric might be built up as follows:

In 1 m² of wall:

0.30	m³	Concrete	@	$106.00	=	$31.80
2.00	m²	Formwork	@	$43.05	=	86.10
13.45	kg	Reinforcing steel	@	$1.05	=	14.12
		Total cost per m²				$132.02

A similar calculation for a project designed in imperial would be:

In 1 SF of wall:

0.037	CY	Concrete	@	$81.10	=	$3.00
2.00	SF	Formwork	@	$4.00	=	8.00
2.75	lbs	Reinforcing steel	@	$0.48	=	1.32
		Total cost per SF				$12.32

Besides measuring and pricing walls in this way, a number of components in a building can be treated in a similar fashion to build up a total cost. A distinct benefit of this approach is that it is easy to make adjustments in the cost when, say, it is decided to make a change from a reinforced concrete to a block wall. No adjustment is needed to the quantity, only a change from one unit price to another. Whenever possible the measurement is simplified and the unit prices are calculated to include all the small miscellaneous items normally measured separately in the quantity survey method.

The main advantages of the unit in place method are that it is quite accurate, it takes into account the peculiarities of the building such as its size, shape, quality and type of construction, and because it identifies the costs of the systems and materials in the building it can be of help in controlling cost in the later stages of design. It is also the only method, other than the quantity survey method, which can be used for estimating the cost of alteration work.

Its disadvantages are that it takes considerably more time than any single-rate method, and it needs a certain amount of design information before it can be used. It cannot be used, for instance, at the sketch drawing stage, except perhaps for some items, because there is insufficient design information available at that time to measure unit in place quantities. In fact, any attempt to measure these quantities at that stage is likely to result in a great many items being overlooked, leading to an inaccurate estimate.

Typical Bay Method

In the typical bay method, a typical bay is measured and priced in detail using the quantity survey method or the unit in place method, and the cost of the bay is multiplied by the total number of bays in the building to give a total cost for the building. As an estimating method its major defect is that it is not usually easy to identify a typical bay, and so many adjustments have to be made for non-typical bays that the estimate can get out of control. It is, however, useful for comparing the costs of different structural or cladding systems. Estimates of typical bays comparing several alternative designs will indicate which of them are the more economical and might be given further consideration, and which should be discarded immediately.

This method is not therefore recommended as a total estimating method but, because it is quite fast and accurate as a means of comparing costs, it can be useful at the design development stage in helping to make design decisions.

Elemental Method

The final multiple-rate method is the elemental method which will be described in the next three chapters.

CHAPTER 4

Elemental Cost Analysis

COST ANALYSIS

No matter which estimating method is used, an analysis of known construction costs is needed to provide the necessary information for future estimates. Furthermore, the estimating method to be used will automatically dictate the way in which costs have to be analyzed. If it is proposed to use the square metre or square foot method of estimating, then the analyses must be recorded as costs per square metre or per square foot and there is little point in recording them in any other form. There is therefore a close affinity between a cost analysis and the estimating method for which it will be used.

In fact, the only difference between the analysis of any of the single-rate methods and the estimate produced from the analysis is the difference between division and multiplication. For the square metre or square foot method, for example, the known cost of a building is divided by its gross floor area to arrive at its cost per unit of area (the analysis), while the gross floor area of a proposed building is multiplied by the known cost per unit of area obtained from the analysis to arrive at a total cost (the estimate).

In the case of multiple-rate methods the same principle applies, but because there are multiple unit rates an analysis has to be performed on each of the rates. In the quantity survey method described in the last chapter, for example, the cost of hanging a door was found by dividing the daily cost of a crew of workers by the number of doors they are expected to hang in a day. The result can be multiplied by the total number of doors in a proposed building to estimate the total cost of hanging them. As each item is analyzed a library of cost analyses can be built up and used for future estimates, bearing in mind of course that cost analyses can soon become out of date and have to be revised as labour rates and material prices change.

ELEMENTAL COST ANALYSIS

The estimating methods described in the last chapter were either too simple or too detailed. Any alternative, if it is to be an improvement over the other methods, should be less detailed than the quantity survey or unit in place methods, yet it should not be so limited as to make it little better than one of the single-rate methods.

An elemental cost analysis is designed to meet these criteria. It is used to provide cost information for an elemental estimate or cost plan and, since it is a multiple-rate method, it requires a form of breakdown. A breakdown which might occur immediately to contractors is a breakdown by trades because they are used to thinking about building costs in terms of trades. If they were to analyze all the buildings they tender, recording the cost of each trade as a percentage of the total or as a cost per square unit of the gross floor area, it is conceivable that they might build up a useful library of cost information. But an elemental cost analysis is first needed in the pre-tender period to help provide a budget estimate in the very early stages of design, a time when the architects and their consultants have given little thought to many of the actual materials which will be used in the building. An analysis based on a trade breakdown is not going to be of much use in preparing the estimate at this stage because the materials to be used will be largely unknown.

An alternative to a trade breakdown is a breakdown of costs by systems or elements. Every building can be seen to consist not only a collection of materials but also as a collection of elements, each of which performs a specific function for the building. One such element is the exterior walls enclosing the building. The primary function of the exterior walls is to exclude the weather from the building, with possible secondary functions of supporting the floors and roof and providing a pleasing external appearance. The primary function of the wall is always the same, regardless of what it is made of. In the early stages of design it will be known that an exterior wall is required, but little or no thought may have been given to its composition.

It is usually only later in the design process that the decision is made whether it should be made of brick, stone, concrete or some other material. A cost analysis which identifies the cost of an element such as the exterior walls is of more use when setting a budget than a breakdown which identifies the cost of say, masonry. All buildings have exterior walls but in the early stages of the design it isn't known whether or where masonry will be used. An elemental breakdown enables a budget to be set for a building before the materials have been selected because the budget is based on known elements, rather than on unknown materials.

Elemental cost analysis and cost control was originally developed in the United Kingdom in the late 1950s. In Canada an elemental breakdown for cost planning was first developed in 1963 by a few consulting quantity surveyors. Although it was based on the breakdown used in the United Kingdom, it was sufficiently different to make it uniquely Canadian and was thought to be an improvement over the U.K. model.

In 1971 the Canadian Institute of Quantity Surveyors formed a sub-committee to review the elemental breakdown being used by quantity surveyors across the country and early in 1972 the Institute published the first edition of its *Elemental Cost Analysis – Method of Measurement and Pricing* which standardized the breakdown and was used by consulting quantity surveyors over the next twenty years.

By the middle 1980s it was felt that the breakdown needed to be updated to reflect current practice and after lengthy consultation and discussion the current breakdown was approved in 1993 and incorporated in the second edition of *Elemental Cost Analysis – Method of Measurement and Pricing*.

In the United States *Uniformat*, a system of classification of building elements quite similar to the Canadian elemental breakdown, was published in the 1970s by the General Services Administration and the American Institute of Architects. In recent years its value has been recognized, not just for cost analysis and cost control, but also for value engineering and outline and performance specifications. It is expected that, under the aegis of the Construction Specifications Institute, this will be updated and renamed *CSI/CSC UniFormat* and be published in conjunction with *Masterformat*, possibly making it the standard for the whole of North America.

An element has been defined as "a major component common to most buildings which usually performs the same function or functions irrespective of its design, construction or specification." Note that in this context `function' refers to the function performed by the component in the building, not to the function of the building itself. In selecting a list of elements as a breakdown for cost analysis the primary aim therefore is to ensure that each element performs a readily identifiable function within the building. Coupled with this, each element should have a significant cost, and wherever possible should be capable of measurement. The current list of elements, which fulfils these requirements, is shown in Figure 2.

The elements are divided into five major groups consisting of `Shell', `Interiors', `Services', `Site & Ancillary Work' and `General Requirements & Allowances'. These groups are identified by alphabetical prefixes, following the *CSI/CSC UniFormat*'s system. This is because when *CSI/CSC UniFormat* is published it is intended to recognize trade headings by their numerical prefixes, while elemental headings will be recognized by their alphabetical prefixes. It is also intended eventually to have elemental listings for other structures such as highways, processing facilities, bridges and dams as well as for buildings. The major group elements A - D would then be used for buildings, elements E - Y would be for the other structures, and Z would be the group of elements applicable to all types of structures.

Within each major group are the Group Elements such as `Substructure' and `Structure' which are further divided into the basic functional elements which can be found in most buildings such as `Foundations' and `Lowest Floor Construction'.

Finally, some of the elements are further sub-divided to identify their contents. Although they are referred to as sub-elements, in most instances they are not elements as defined above because they do not perform a recognizable function within the building, but they do provide useful sub-groupings within elements. `Foundations' for example is an element because foundations provide a specific function for the building. The

LIST OF ELEMENTS

A SHELL
  A1 Substructure
    A11 Foundations
      A111 Standard Foundations
      A112 Special Foundations
    A12 Basement Excavation
  A2 Structure
    A21 Lowest Floor Construction
    A22 Upper Floor Construction
      A221 Upper Floor Construction
      A222 Stair Construction
    A23 Roof Construction
  A3 Exterior Enclosure
    A31 Walls Below Grade
      A311 Walls Below Grade
      A312 Structural Walls Below Grade
    A32 Walls Above Grade
      A321 Walls Above Grade
      A322 Structural Walls Above Grade
      A323 Curtain Walls
    A33 Windows & Entrances
      A331 Windows & Louvres
      A332 Glazed Screens
      A333 Doors
    A34 Roof Covering
      A341 Roofing
      A342 Skylights & Roof Glazing
    A35 Projections

B INTERIORS
  B1 Partitions & Doors
    B11 Partitions
      B111 Fixed Partitions
      B112 Movable Partitions
      B113 Structural Partitions
    B12 Doors
  B2 Finishes
    B21 Floor Finishes
    B22 Ceiling Finishes
    B23 Wall Finishes
  B3 Fittings & Equipment
    B31 Fittings & Fixtures
      B311 Metals
      B312 Millwork
      B313 Specialties
      B314 Furnishings

Figure 2

LIST OF ELEMENTS (Continued)

B32   Equipment
B33   Conveying Systems
     B331   Elevators
     B332   Escalators & Moving Walks
     B333   Material Handling Systems

C   SERVICES
 C1 Mechanical
     C11   Plumbing and Drainage
        C111   Equipment
        C112   Piping
        C113   Fixtures
        C114   Special Piping & Fixtures
     C12   Fire Protection
        C121   Equipment
        C122   Piping & Sprinkler Heads
     C13   HVAC
        C131   Equipment
        C132   Ductwork
        C133   Piping
        C134   Ductwork Terminal Devices
        C135   Piping Terminal Devices
     C14   Controls
        C141   Central Equipment
        C142   Control Points
 C2 Electrical
     C21   Service & Distribution
        C211   Equipment
        C212   Auxiliary Power Equipment
        C213   Distribution
        C214   Motor Controls
     C22   Lighting, Devices & Heating
        C221   Lighting
        C222   Devices
        C223   Heating
     C23   Systems & Ancillaries
        C231   Fire Alarm
        C232   Communications
        C233   Security
        C234   Other Systems & Ancillaries

Figure 2 (Continued)

LIST OF ELEMENTS (Continued)

```
D   SITE & ANCILLARY WORK
    D1  Site Work
        D11     Site Development
                D111    Preparation
                D112    Hard Surfaces
                D113    Improvements
                D114    Landscaping
        D12     Site Mechanical
        D13     Site Electrical
    D2  Ancillary Work
        D21     Demolition
                D211    Demolition
                D212    Hazardous Materials
        D22     Alterations

Z   GENERAL REQUIREMENTS & ALLOWANCES
    Z1  General Requirements & Fee
        Z11     General Requirements
                Z111    Supervision
                Z112    Temporary Conditions
                Z113    Permits, Insurance & Bonds
        Z12     Fee
    Z2  Allowances
        Z21     Design Allowance
        Z22     Escalation Allowance
        Z23     Construction Allowance
```

Figure 2 (Concluded)

sub-elements `Standard Foundations' and `Special Foundations' on the other hand are not elements, they merely identify the costs of two types of foundations.

The breakdown therefore consists of four levels of information for a cost analysis as follows:

Level 1   Major Group Elements
Level 2   Group Elements
Level 3   Elements
Level 4   Sub-Elements

This breakdown of elements should be adhered to rigidly for a cost analysis, with a zero or dash entered against any element for which there is no cost. However, as will be described in the next chapter, a substantially reduced format can usually be used for an estimate or cost plan. It is intended to be used for both new construction and for renovations, although each would require a separate analysis.

The first group of elements under `Shell' is `Substructure' which incorporates those elements to be found below grade. The function of `Foundations' is to support the building and its cost will vary depending on the height and loading of the building, and the soil conditions on the site.

Not all buildings have a basement, so a separate element is included for `Basement Excavation' to identify the cost of excavating and backfilling for a basement and to allow the analysis to be used for buildings both with and without basements.

The second group of elements, `Structure', contains the horizontal structural elements. `Lowest Floor Construction' is usually a slab on grade, but it can be a suspended slab with a crawl space below it.

`Upper Floor Construction' covers the main structural components of the building including any ancillary items which are associated with them. The sub-element `Stair Construction' identifies the cost of stairs in a building. Although stairs perform a specific function within the building and might therefore be considered to qualify as an element, their cost is not usually significant enough to warrant their being made an element.

`Roof Construction' is the structural cost of providing a roof over the building. Although it is usually located at the highest point of a building it can also be found at grade level if the basement projects beyond the main body of the building, or at any point between if the building has set-backs.

`Exterior Enclosure' has those elements which perform the function of providing an envelope around the building. It might be thought that `Walls Below Grade' which enclose basement areas below grade should be included under `Substructure' on the grounds that these walls are, as their name implies, below grade. This would ignore the primary function of `Walls Below Grade' which is not to support the building as the foundations do, but to enclose the building in the same way as `Walls Above Grade'. `Walls Above Grade' happen to keep out the wind and weather while `Walls Below Grade' keep out the surrounding soil and the function of each is essentially the same.

Both `Walls Below Grade' and `Walls Above Grade' contain sub-elements identifying the structural components of the walls. The identification of structural walls (or any other peculiarity) within an element can be made in one of two ways – by cost or by description. A structural wall above grade will be more expensive than a non-structural wall and the fact that the walls in one building have a higher cost than the walls in another building is an indication that one may have structural walls while the other doesn't. The alternative is to have separate sub-elements identifying the cost of the structural components of the walls, giving an immediate and unambiguous indication in the analysis of whether the building contains structural walls, and this has been done for both `Walls Below Grade' and `Walls Above Grade'. In addition, `Walls Above Grade' has a sub-element to identify the cost of curtain walls.

`Windows & Entrances' includes windows, louvres, glazed screens, and entrances and doors which are to be found in the vertical exterior cladding.

`Roof Covering' is the horizontal element of the building envelope including roofing and those components normally associated with the roof such as soffits, roof hatches, skylights and roof glazing. As with `Roof Construction' this element is not always found only at the highest point of the building.

`Projections' incorporates those items which add to the cost of the building enclosure, such as balconies, canopies and parapets, but which are not provided for in any of the other exterior enclosure elements.

The first group of elements under `Interiors' is `Partitions & Doors'. These elements encompass any components which divide space within the building, including railings and internal shear walls. Although concrete shear walls might be considered structural because they are used to help support the floors and roof, their primary function is to divide space. The interior planning of the building is not modified to suit the structural engineer's requirements for shear walls, and they can be included in the design only when they fit into the interior planning. An internal structural shear wall therefore can only be used when it is performing the function of a partition. As with `Walls Below Grade' and `Walls Above Grade' provision for identifying the cost of structural shear walls is made by having the sub-element `Structural Partitions' in the cost analysis.

The next group of elements, `Finishes', includes all the interior finishes in the building with the exception of finishes which are an integral part of another element, such as finishes to doors or millwork. Wallboard on walls is also considered to be an integral part of the wall and not to be a finish.

'Fittings & Equipment' incorporates under 'Fittings & Fixtures' such items as millwork and miscellaneous metals which are normally found in a construction contract. Similarly, 'Equipment' includes any equipment such as kitchen or laboratory equipment which is to be supplied and installed under the construction contract. Clients vary with regard to these two elements, some building owners preferring to purchase some or all of the fittings and equipment separately, while others prefer to have them all included in the construction contract, and it is worth noting this with the analysis.

'Conveying Systems' covers elevators, escalators and material handling equipment used to move people and materials around the building.

The next major group is 'Services' which includes all the mechanical and electrical services within the building. Although 'Mechanical' and 'Electrical' are elements they also happen to be trades. Generally the sub-elements within these elements have been classified into:

1. Equipment, including all equipment required for mechanical or electrical services.
2. Distribution systems, including piping, ductwork, wiring etc. required to distribute mechanical and electrical services from the equipment to the terminal devices.
3. Terminal devices, including plumbing fixtures, VAV boxes, fan coils, grilles or diffusers, light fixtures etc.

'Site & Ancillary Work' covers all the work on the site outside the building perimeter. As noted earlier, the elemental breakdown can be used for either new construction or for renovations, although separate analyses should be made for each of them. When the analysis is for a new building 'Demolition' would cover the demolition of any existing structure on the site to make way for the new construction and 'Alterations' would include only those renovations, such as filling in openings or cutting new openings and installing doors in an existing exterior wall, required for an addition to an existing building. Any renovations inside the existing building not attributable directly to the addition would be included in a separate elemental analysis.

An analysis for the renovation of an existing building would have all the costs of demolition needed to prepare for the new work included in 'Demolition', but no costs would need to be allocated to 'Alterations' because they would be included under the appropriate elements. For example, the cost of demolishing partitions and doors in an existing building would be included in 'Demolition' together with any other demolition required for the alterations, but any new partitions, doors and finishes needed to replace them would be included under 'Partitions & Doors' and 'Finishes'.

'General Requirements & Allowances' is, strictly speaking, not an element since it does not perform a function in the building. However, it is part of the total cost of the building and should therefore be included as part of the analysis. 'General Requirements & Fee' contains those costs which the general contractor has to include in its tender to cover overheads, both on the site and for its head office, and the profit it hopes to make. 'Allowances' will be discussed in more detail in the next chapter since they are not normally included in an analysis.

A more detailed description of the elements is given in *Elemental Cost Analysis – Method of Measurement and Pricing*.

Having decided on the form of breakdown, the next step is to provide a means of showing the costs. A lump sum amount against each of the elements in the breakdown might be of some use if every building were the same size, but since no two buildings are alike the cost of each element has to be expressed in a way which will make it useful for future use. This might be done by calculating the percentage each element represents of the total cost of the building. This is frequently done with mechanical and electrical costs, usually as a check to see whether they appear to be adequate when putting together a pre-tender estimate, but percentages

Cost Analysis

Project: District Library		Project No. 93175	
Gross Floor Area: 2,673m²	Architect: Tracer, Print Associates	Date: May 1993	

		Cost per m²	
Element	Amount	Gross	Amount
A SHELL			
A1 Substructure			
A11 Foundations			
A111 Standard Foundations	230,500	86.23	
A112 Special Foundations	—	— $86.23	$230,500
A12 Basement Excavation	—	— —	—
A2 Structure			
A21 Lowest Floor Construction		$30.19	$80,700
A22 Upper Floor Construction			
A221 Upper Floor Construction	188,200	70.41	
A222 Stair Construction	22,200	8.31 $78.71	$210,400
A23 Roof Construction		$94.01	$251,300
A3 Exterior Enclosure			
A31 Walls Below Grade			
A311 Walls Below Grade	—	—	
A312 Structural Walls Below Grade	—	— —	—
A32 Exterior Enclosure			
A321 Walls Above Grade	439,900	164.57	
A322 Structural Walls Above Grade	—	—	
A323 Curtain Walls	—	— $164.57	$439,900
A33 Windows & Entrances			
A331 Windows & Louvres	80,300	30.23	
A332 Glazed Screens	3,900	1.46	
A333 Doors	3,300	1.23 $32.92	$88,000
A34 Roof Covering			
A341 Roofing	215,300	80.55	
A342 Skylights & Roof Glazing	111,400	41.68 $122.22	$326,700
A35 Projections		$2.06	$5,500
B INTERIORS			
B1 Partitions & Doors			
B11 Partitions			
B111 Fixed Partitions	167,400	62.63	
B112 Movable Partitions	27,000	10.10	
B113 Structural Partitions	—	— $72.73	$194,400
B12 Doors		$9.39	$25,100
Carried Forward		$693.04	$1,852,500

Figure 3

can be misleading. When checking mechanical and electrical estimates, for instance, it is not always clear whether their costs may appear to be low because too much money has been spent on the rest of the building, or because they have been underestimated. This will apply with even more force if all the elements are calculated as percentages since a particularly high (or low) percentage in any one element will distort the percentages of all the other elements and make comparisons between one building and another difficult.

A more suitable way of expressing the cost is to show the cost of each element as its cost per square metre or per square foot of the gross floor area. The analysis is then not unlike the square metre method described in the last chapter, except that instead of just the total cost of the building being divided by the gross floor area to give a total cost per unit of area, each of the elements is divided by the gross floor area to give a series of costs per unit of gross floor area.

Figure 3, which is part of a computer spreadsheet, shows the first page of the cost analysis of a district library in which the costs have been analyzed in this way. It is based on a building designed in metric but a building designed in imperial can be analyzed in exactly the same way by substituting square feet for square metres. The gross floor area is 2,673 m² and the total cost of this page is $1,852,500, which gives a cost of $693.04 per m². Of this the `Windows & Entrances', for example, contributed $88,000 or $32.92 per m², and within `Windows & Entrances' the `Doors' contributed $3,300 or $1.23 per m². Recorded against each element and sub-element is its total cost and its cost per square metre of the gross floor area. Note that the costs are all recorded to the nearest hundred dollars which is close enough for an analysis. It is also close enough for an estimate and helps guard against delusions of accuracy.

A budget estimate can now be made using this basic information, particularly if the known costs of several buildings have been analyzed in this way and provided they are reasonably up-to-date. The gross floor area can be measured and, instead of having to select a gross area cost for the whole building, a gross area cost cost for each of the elements can be selected from the analyses and a total cost built up. It is easier to build up a total in this way than it is to select a single unit cost for the complete building. It also overcomes the principal disadvantage of the single-rate methods because it is possible to allow in the estimate for differences in size, quality and type of construction.

Although analyzing the cost of each element to give a unit cost of the gross floor area for each is a step in the right direction, there are further analyses which can be made and which can be even more useful. One of the objectives in selecting the list of elements was that, wherever possible, each element should be capable of measurement. Figure 4 shows the next stage in the analysis of the library in which quantities for many of the major elements have been shown under the `Quantity' column. They were measured when the detailed estimate was done just prior to tender and while they are `gross' figures they should be accurate. The way in which measurements are made for each element is described in *Elemental Cost Analysis – Method of Measurement and Pricing*. The quantities for `Floor Finishes' and `Ceiling Finishes' should include those usable areas for which there is no finish and therefore no cost. This is to provide an indication of the total usable space in the building and will be explained later when ratios are discussed.

When the amount of each element is divided by the quantity, the result is the unit rate shown in the `Unit Rate' column. Although the amount is derived from a variety of materials and trades which make up the cost of an element, the unit rate gives an overall unit cost based on the quantity of the element, and gives a general indication of the standard of quality used. Care should be taken not to confuse this rate with the unit cost of the gross floor area, the former being the amount divided by the quantity of the element, while the latter is the amount divided by the gross floor area.

With a unit rate for most of the elements, preliminary estimating becomes more accurate when sketch drawings are available, since it is possible at least to measure the area of the foundations, the cube of the basement, if there is one, and the areas of the floors, roof and exterior enclosure. Then, instead of trying to estimate the cost of each element by using the cost per unit of the gross floor area, the elements themselves are measured as far as possible and unit rates applied, allowing the shape of the building to be taken into account. For those elements which cannot

Cost Analysis

Project: District Library			Project No. 93175	
Gross Floor Area: 2,673m²	Architect: Tracer, Print Associates		Date: May 1993	

Element	Quantity	Unit Rate	Amount	Cost per m² Gross	Amount
A SHELL					
A1 Substructure					
A11 Foundations					
A111 Standard Foundations	1,561 m²	147.66	230,500	86.23	
A112 Special Foundations	—	—	—	—	$86.23 $230,500
A12 Basement Excavation	—	—	—	—	— —
A2 Structure					
A21 Lowest Floor Construction	1,561 m²	51.70			$30.19 $80,700
A22 Upper Floor Construction					
A221 Upper Floor Construction	1,112 m²	169.24	188,200	70.41	
A222 Stair Construction	92 m	241.30	22,200	8.31	$78.71 $210,400
A23 Roof Construction	1,690 m²	148.70			$94.01 $251,300
A3 Exterior Enclosure					
A31 Walls Below Grade					
A311 Walls Below Grade	—	—	—	—	
A312 Structural Walls Below Grade	—	—	—	—	— —
A32 Exterior Enclosure					
A321 Walls Above Grade	1,675 m²	262.63	439,900	164.57	
A322 Structural Walls Above Grade	—	—	—	—	
A323 Curtain Walls	—	—	—	—	$164.57 $439,900
A33 Windows & Entrances					
A331 Windows & Louvres	208 m²	388.46	80,300	30.23	
A332 Glazed Screens	7 m²	557.14	3,900	1.46	
A333 Doors	9 m²	366.67	3,300	1.23	$32.92 $88,000
A34 Roof Covering					
A341 Roofing	1,559 m²	138.10	215,300	80.55	
A342 Skylights & Roof Glazing	131 m²	850.38	111,400	41.68	$122.22 $326,700
A35 Projections	30 m²	183.33			$2.06 $5,500
B INTERIORS					
B1 Partitions & Doors					
B11 Partitions					
B111 Fixed Partitions	2,098 m²	79.79	167,400	62.63	
B112 Movable Partitions	53 m²	509.43	27,000	10.10	
B113 Structural Partitions	—	—	—	—	$72.73 $194,400
B12 Doors	80 m²	313.75			$9.39 $25,100
Carried Forward					$693.04 $1,852,500

Figure 4

be measured, the cost is derived from lump sum amounts, from the unit cost of the gross floor area or by the use of ratios, which will be described later.

A problem which occurs with any form of cost analysis is that the costs soon become out of date. One solution is to analyze the quantities in the detailed estimate on which the analysis is based and to re-price them from time to time to update the unit rate. For example, the unit rate of $147.66 for `Standard Foundations' in Figure 4, while it is actually calculated by dividing $230,500 by 1,561 m^2, is also made up of priced quantities as follows:

Excavation	1.6208 m^3 @	$9.45 =	$15.32
Backfill	1.4202 m^3 @	$15.75 =	22.37
Dewatering			2.02
Concrete	0.1634 m^3 @	$136.50 =	22.30
Formwork to footings	0.2614 m^2 @	$56.70 =	14.82
Formwork to walls	0.6201 m^2 @	$68.25 =	42.32
Reinforcing steel	11.3517 kg @	$1.26 =	14.30
300mm Concrete block	0.1262 m^2 @	$99.75 =	12.59
Perimeter insulation	0.0833 m^2 @	$19.43 =	1.62
			$147.66

Each of the quantities is derived by dividing the actual quantity in the detailed estimate by the area of the element, in this case by 1,561 m^2, and the quantities are then priced at the rates used in the estimate. The unit rate can be updated at any time by re-pricing the quantities at current prices. This is a tedious exercise and probably not worth the effort since costs can easily be updated with the help of cost indexes, although with the advent of computers it may become more viable. Although this example is given in metric the same approach can be used for an imperial project.

Wherever a quantity can be shown against an element it can be divided by the gross floor area to give a ratio. Figure 5 shows the completed cost analysis sheet for the district library with the ratios shown in the `Ratio' column. The ratios can serve three useful purposes. First, they provide a means of checking for mathematical errors. For example, the ratios of `Lowest Floor Construction' and `Upper Floor Construction' should always total 1.0 because the quantities of these two elements when added together are equal to the total gross floor area. With experience of a number of analyses and estimates over a period of time the ratios of other elements become familiar, and if an unexpected ratio appears it would be wise to check the quantity to see if it is correct.

Second, the ratio will show why one building is more expensive than another. While the quality and type of construction of two buildings may be very similar, giving similar unit rates for the elements, the total costs may be quite different. A review of the ratios will show why this is so; perhaps the more expensive building has a less efficient shape, or contains proportionately more partitions, or has higher storey heights, and a comparison of the ratios will immediately indicate this.

Third, the ratio can be used in very early estimates as a means of establishing a quantity for an element. This applies particularly to partitions and finishes when a preliminary drawing may indicate the overall size and shape of the building, but doesn't show how the interior will be sub-divided. The ratios contained in an analysis of a similar type of building can be used to provide the missing quantities which, while they won't be exact, should be reasonably close. Also, it can be seen that the ratio of an element multiplied by its unit rate equals its cost per unit of gross floor area, which gives an alternative way of calculating the amount. Instead of finding the quantity by using the ratio and then multiplying it by the unit rate, multiply the ratio by

Cost Analysis

Project:	District Library					Project No. 93175
Gross Floor Area: 2,673m²		Architect: Tracer, Print Associates				Date: May 1993

Element	Ratio	Quantity	Unit Rate	Amount	Cost per m² Gross	Amount
A SHELL						
A1 Substructure						
A11 Foundations						
A111 Standard Foundations	0.58	1,561 m²	147.66	230,500	86.23	
A112 Special Foundations	—	—	—	—	—	$86.23 $230,500
A12 Basement Excavation	—	—	—	—	—	—
A2 Structure						
A21 Lowest Floor Construction	0.58	1,561 m²	51.70			$30.19 $80,700
A22 Upper Floor Construction						
A221 Upper Floor Construction	0.42	1,112 m²	169.24	188,200	70.41	
A222 Stair Construction	0.03	92 m	241.30	22,200	8.31	$78.71 $210,400
A23 Roof Construction	0.63	1,690 m²	148.70			$94.01 $251,300
A3 Exterior Enclosure						
A31 Walls Below Grade						
A311 Walls Below Grade	—	—	—	—	—	
A312 Structural Walls Below Grade	—	—	—	—	—	— —
A32 Exterior Enclosure						
A321 Walls Above Grade	0.63	1,675 m²	262.63	439,900	164.57	
A322 Structural Walls Above Grade	—	—	—	—	—	
A323 Curtain Walls	—	—	—	—	—	$164.57 $439,900
A33 Windows & Entrances						
A331 Windows & Louvres	0.08	208 m²	388.46	80,300	30.23	
A332 Glazed Screens	0.00	7 m²	557.14	3,900	1.46	
A333 Doors	0.00	9 m²	366.67	3,300	1.23	$32.92 $88,000
A34 Roof Covering						
A341 Roofing	0.58	1,559 m²	138.10	215,300	80.55	
A342 Skylights & Roof Glazing	0.05	131 m²	850.38	111,400	41.68	$122.22 $326,700
A35 Projections	0.00	30 m²	183.33			$2.06 $5,500
B INTERIORS						
B1 Partitions & Doors						
B11 Partitions						
B111 Fixed Partitions	0.78	2,098 m²	79.79	167,400	62.63	
B112 Movable Partitions	0.02	53 m²	509.43	27,000	10.10	
B113 Structural Partitions	—	—	—	—	—	$72.73 $194,400
B12 Doors	0.03	80 m²	313.75			$9.39 $25,100
Carried Forward						$693.04 $1,852,500

Figure 5

	Cost Analysis							
Project:	District Library						Project No. 93175	
	Element	Ratio	Quantity	Unit Rate	Amount	Cost per m² Gross		Amount
	Brought Forward						$693.04	$1,852,500
B2	Finishes							
	B21 Floor Finishes	0.93	2,490 m²	66.43			$61.88	$165,400
	B22 Ceiling Finishes	0.93	2,490 m²	57.63			$53.68	$143,500
	B23 Wall Finishes	1.32	3,529 m²	14.25			$18.82	$50,300
B3	Fittings & Equipment							
	B31 Fittings & Fixtures							
	B311 Metals				15,500	5.80		
	B312 Millwork				52,700	19.72		
	B313 Specialties				4,500	1.68		
	B314 Furniture				–	–	$27.20	$72,700
	B32 Equipment						–	–
	B33 Conveying Systems							
	B331 Elevators		1 No.	84,0000	84,000	31.43		
	B332 Escalators & Moving Walks		–	–	–	–		
	B333 Material Handling Systems		–	–	–	–	$31.43	$84,000
C	SERVICES							
C1	Mechanical							
	C11 Plumbing & Drainage							
	C111 Equipment				6,300	2.36		
	C112 Piping				59,200	22.15		
	C113 Fixtures				18,900	7.07		
	C114 Special Piping & Fixtures				–	–	$31.58	84,400
	C12 Fire Protection							
	C121 Equipment				7,100	2.66		
	C122 Piping & Sprinkler Heads				43,500	16.27	$18.93	$50,600
	C13 HVAC							
	C131 Equipment				119,800	44.82		
	C132 Ductwork				70700	26.45		
	C133 Piping				82,700	30.94		
	C134 Ductwork Terminal Devices				13,500	5.05		
	C135 Piping Terminal Devices				16,900	6.32	$113.66	$303,800
	C14 Controls							
	C141 Central Equipment				5,600	2.10		
	C142 Control Points				28,100	10.51	$12.61	33,700
	Carried Forward						$1,062.81	$2,840,900

Figure 5 (Continued)

Cost Analysis

Project: District Library						**Project No. 93175**

Element	Ratio	Quantity	Unit Rate	Amount	Cost per m² Gross	Amount
Brought Forward					$1,062.81	$2,840,900
C2 Electrical						
C21 Services & Distribution						
C211 Equipment				15,800	5.91	
C212 Auxiliary Power Equipment				—	—	
C213 Distribution				26,200	9.80	
C214 Motor Controls				11,600	4.34	$20.05	$53,600
C22 Lighting, Devices & Heating						
C221 Lighting				124,400	46.54	
C222 Devices				36,800	13.77	
C223 Heating				—	—	$60.31	$161,200
C23 Systems & Ancillaries						
C231 Fire Alarm				28,900	10.81	
C232 Communications				4,200	1.57	
C233 Security				6,300	2.36	
C234 Other Systems & Ancillaries				26,200	9.80	$24.54	$65,600
D SITE & ANCILLARY WORK						
D1 Site Work						
D11 Site Development						
D111 Preparation		1,906 m²	2.10	4,000	1.50	
D112 Hard Surfaces		4,681 m²	30.76	144,000	53.87	
D113 Improvements				10,300	3.85	
D114 Landscaping				78,800	29.48	$88.70	$237,100
D12 Mechanical Site Services						$17.70	$47,300
D13 Electrical Site Services						$17.28	$46,200
D2 Ancillary Work						
D21 Demolition						
D211 Demolition				—	—	
D212 Hazardous Materials				—	—	—	—
D22 Alterations				—	—	—	—
Carried Forward					$1,291.40	$3,451,900

Figure 5 (Continued)

Cost Analysis

Project:	District Library						Project No. 93175

Element	Ratio	Quantity	Unit Rate	Amount	Cost per m² Gross	Amount
Brought Forward					$1,291.40	$3,451,900
Z GENERAL REQUIREMENTS & ALLOWANCES						
Z1 General Requirements & Fee						
Z11 General Requirements						
Z111 Supervision & Labour Expenses				88,500	33.11	
Z112 Temporary Conditions				164,500	61.54	
Z113 Permits, Insurance & Bonds				15,800	5.91	$100.56	$268,800
Z12 Fee					$25.14	$67,200
Z2 Allowances						
Z21 Design Allowance				—	—	—
Z22 Escalation Allowance				—	—	—
Z23 Construction Allowance				—	—	—
Total					$1,417.06	$3,787,900

Notes:

A2 - Reinforced concrete structure.

A32 - 92% brick with ornamental features. 8% stone facing, stucco and metal siding.

A341 - Felt and gravel plus curved metal and pyramid structures.

A35 - Roof and floor overhangs plus an entrance canopy.

B111 - 52% block, 6% glazed screens, 45% metal stud.

B21 - 90% carpet.

B22 - 91% painted gypsum board, 9% lay-in tile.

C232 - Conduit only.

C233 - Conduit only.

Figure 5 (Concluded)

Project No. _____   Date _____

Project _____

Client _____

Location _____

Building Type _____

Type of Contract _____ Tender Date _____

Market Conditions _____ Index _____ Source _____

Site (Urban, Rural etc.) _____ Number of Tenders ____

Tender Range: Low $_____   High $_____

Length of Construction   ____ Months

Number of Storeys: Below Grade ____   Above Grade ____

Gross Floor Areas: Basement   _____ m²

                         Ground Floor   _____ m²

                         Upper Floors   _____ m²

                         Penthouse   _____ m²

                         Total   _____ m²

Window Ratio _____   Wall Finish Ratio _____

Sketch:

Analysis prepared by   _____

Figure 6

the unit rate, and then multiply the result by the gross floor area to arrive at a total cost for the element.

Finally, if the quantities for `Floor Finishes' and `Ceiling Finishes' include those usable areas for which there is no finish this will generate ratios for these elements which can be used to convert net areas to gross areas when preparing an estimate or cost plan at the program stage. Cement finishes, for example, are included with their slabs, not with `Floor Finishes' and, if they don't have an applied finish on them, might not be expected to be included in the area of `Floor Finishes'. Similarly, a space which has no ceiling has no area or cost for `Ceiling Finishes'. Unless these areas are included, although no cost would be applied to them, the ratios for these two elements will be of no use for an estimate at the program stage.

The notes at the end of the analysis can be used to record specifications, inclusions, exclusions or other peculiarities about the building for future reference. Figure 6 shows another form which can accompany the analysis to provide additional information about the building and the tenders which were received. The Window ratio is intended to show the windows as a ratio of the total vertical exterior cladding. This can be used to calculate the area of windows when only block plans are available for a preliminary estimate or cost plan. The Wall Finish ratio performs the same function for wall finishes. Based on the assumption that wall finishes are applied to the inside face of the exterior walls and to both faces of the partitions, but that duct shafts and ceiling spaces and the like will not be finished, it is useful to record the ratio of the actual area of wall finishes to the total areas of `Walls Below Grade' and `Walls Above Grade', plus twice times the area of `Partitions and Doors'. This can be used for calculating the area of wall finishes when only block plans are available for a future estimate or cost plan. Although space is provided in Figure 6 for a sketch of the building it may be more useful in some instances to attach reduced copies of the contract plans and elevations.

The Uses of an Elemental Cost Analysis

An elemental cost analysis has several uses, many of which are not found in other methods of cost analysis. It ensures consistency of format and provides a checklist to ensure that no part of the building is overlooked when it is subsequently used for a budget estimate. Most buildings, whatever their type, contain most of the functional elements.

It shows how the costs are distributed over the building and in doing so shows the importance of any element in the total cost of the building. A review of the figures in the `Cost per m² Gross' column indicates immediately whether an element represents a major part of the cost of the building or whether, in fact, its cost is comparatively insignificant. The architects' aim when designing a building should be to provide a reasonable allocation of costs over the elements, but it takes experience and several analyses of similar buildings to recognize a proper balance of costs between them.

Because the costs of all the elements are reduced to costs per unit of the gross floor area, the costs of the same element in buildings of a similar type but of different sizes can be compared to reveal any discrepancies between them. The floor finishes of the district library, for example, amount to $61.88 per m² and comparison with other libraries shows this to be an acceptable figure.

Lastly, an elemental cost analysis provides useful information for estimating and for planning the cost of future projects. It is possible, although generally not advisable, to prepare an estimate or cost plan using costs per square unit of the gross floor area obtained from elemental cost analyses before any sketch drawings have been developed by the architects. Because the cost plan would have been based on an acceptable quality and type of construction, the drawings and specifications could then be prepared using the cost plan as a guide. This means that design would follow cost rather than the other way round. This approach might be feasible when applied to a building program such as a school building program where a number of buildings of a similar type have been analyzed and a budget has to be established for the coming year, but it is not appropriate for most individual buildings. Although there may be occasions when an estimate has to be prepared in advance of the drawings and specifications, it is advisable to consult the architects and their engineers, if they have been appointed, to get some input from them even though it may only be minimal.

Finally, care is needed when using elemental cost analyses for preliminary estimates and cost plans. Every building is unique, site conditions and market conditions are variable, and recorded costs soon become outdated, which means that while the cost analysis can be useful as a guide, a certain amount of common sense together with a knowledge of current construction costs are needed when forecasting the cost of a proposed building.

CHAPTER 5

Cost Planning

Cost control in the pre-tender period of a construction program should have three main objectives: to ensure that the actual cost of the building does not exceed the owner's budget, to give the owner value for money, and to achieve a proper balance of expenditure over the building elements. If the first of these objectives can be achieved the others will often follow, particularly if the elemental method is used to establish a cost plan in the early design stages to help control costs in the later stages.

It is important to understand what is meant by a cost plan. Although it is similar to an estimate its objectives are different. An estimate is usually thought of as a prediction of cost based on a particular design and the estimate can only be changed if the design is changed. A contractor's estimate, for example, contributes nothing to the design. It reflects what a particular design will cost after all the design decisions have been made and its function is passive. A cost plan on the other hand is intended to be active. It is an estimate, prepared in the early stages of design before all the details of the building have been decided upon, in a form which shows how costs might be distributed throughout the elements of the building. Although it will have been based on certain assumptions, it will not specify in detail how the money is to be spent and is therefore like a budget. A household budget, for example, sets the total amount of money a family can afford to spend during the month. Based on past experience it allocates amounts to be spent on food, clothing, rent, vacations etc., but it does not specify in detail how the money will be spent within each category. If more has to be spent on one category, less will be available to be spent in other categories if the budget is to be maintained, and it is up to the householders to design their spending so that it fits within their budget. In the same way a cost plan sets the amount an owner needs to spend on the building and allocates target costs to the elements without defining the materials and methods making up those costs. It demonstrates how costs *might* be expended within a given total, but does not specify how they *must* be expended, allowing for flexibility of design within the overall cost. Also like a budget a cost plan is intended to help control the costs as the design is developed.

PROGRAM STAGE

To see how the elemental method can be used to plan and control the cost in the pre-tender period of a construction project it helps to consider it within the context of the design process which can be seen as a series of stages, often overlapping, which lead up to the final set of working drawings and specifications to be used by contractors to estimate their costs when submitting tenders. The first of these stages is the program or concept stage. At this stage the potential building owner may have prepared a feasibility study, or have appointed consultants to write a building program, or have approached an architect with an outline of the owners' requirements. Whatever form it might take the result is some description, perhaps a written program, which will indicate the type of building to be built, its location, possibly its overall size, its standard of quality, and the net areas and types of spaces which have to be provided within the building. It is unlikely that any drawings will have been prepared, but if they have they would only show block plans supplementing the program, probably at a small scale, with perhaps some indication of the types of space to be included in very broad outline.

It is likely that building owners would want to discuss costs at this stage. They may have already determined how much they can afford to spend and want to know whether the building they have in mind can be built within the budget. Or they have not yet set the budget and want to know how much money should be allocated for construction. In either case an estimate of the construction cost has to be made. The estimate would not include incidental costs such as design fees or other development expenses which are normally included separately in the building owners' project budget.

This produces an interesting paradox. The first estimate given to a client is possibly the most important in the life of the project. It is the estimate the client will always remember because it gives the first indication of what the construction cost is likely to be, and because it provides information which will form part of a major financial decision including, perhaps, whether the client can afford to build at all. It is also important to the architects because an inadequate estimate at this stage will cause them a great deal of trouble in the future. The first estimate should therefore be as accurate as possible: not so low as to mislead the building owners into continuing with a project which they cannot afford, nor so high as to cause it to be cancelled when it would in fact have been perfectly feasible. At the same time it is the estimate which is based on the least amount of information. The building owners may have a reasonably clear idea of what they wants in their building in terms of accommodation, function and standard of quality, but these are still a long way from being translated into construction terms of bricks and mortar, which is the basis for construction costs.

Although the first estimate must be as accurate as possible, if it is asked for at the program stage it cannot be prepared in great detail because there isn't enough available information. Since there are usually no drawings the estimate must be prepared from the program. If the gross floor area is not given, it has to be calculated from the net areas shown in the program using net to gross floor area ratios. The ratios of `Floor Finishes' or `Ceiling Finishes' shown in a cost analysis can be used for this purpose as a rough guide, but for a more detailed calculation the ratios for different types of space in a publication such as *Means Assemblies Cost Data* published by R.S. Means Company Inc. can be used. The total cost can then be calculated by building it up using costs per unit of gross floor area for each of the elements obtained from cost analyses of previous buildings of a similar type and quality. If architects have been appointed and block plans are available the gross floor area and the areas of some of the elements such as `Roof Construction' and `Exterior Enclosure' can be measured from the plans and unit prices applied to these quantities.

A program-stage estimate has to be based as much on assumptions as on facts, unlike later estimates which can be based more on facts with fewer assumptions. It will tell the client what it is possible for the building to cost and, with proper cost control, what its final cost is likely to be. If the estimate is built up using elemental analyses of previous projects as a guide it can be used as a cost plan because the general standard of quality will have been identified. Most clients recognize the limitations of the first estimate and, provided they are kept informed of their revised cost commitments during the subsequent design stages, will accept minor variations from the first estimate. It is also worth noting that although construction costs are very important to any client, other factors such as a rise in mortgage interest rates can upset a client's budget as much as a variation in construction costs. Very often, too, an upgrading in quality in the later stages of the design of the building, although it will increase construction costs, may give the clients a more acceptable building than they had first visualized, or enable them to charge higher rents to offset the increased cost.

Since the estimate at this stage will be largely based on cost analyses of previous projects, the following adjustments may have to be made to the estimate:

1. TIME

Analyses of previous buildings soon become obsolete and, unless the analyses which are being used for the estimate are very recent, some means will have to be found to update them. A cost index is the usual means of doing this, but many indices which are intended for construction are input rather than output indices. An input index records changes in the costs which contractors have to pay for labour and material and, while this might be of help to a construction company by showing how much its costs are rising or falling, it doesn't reflect changes in productivity or market conditions so it doesn't show changes in the prices submitted by general contractors in their tenders. The *Southam Construction Cost Index* which covers costs in Canada, and the index in *Engineering News Record* which covers costs in the United States and Canada are both input indexes. *Construction Price Statistics* published by Statistics Canada contains both labour and material input cost indices, but it also contains output indices showing changes in costs to the building owner for housing, apartment buildings, office buildings, warehouses, shopping centres, factories and schools in several cities across Canada. The *Boeckh Building Valuation Manual* and *Yardsticks for Costing* also have output indices for a number of Canadian cities.

2. SIZE AND SHAPE

The effect of size, shape and the number of storeys on the cost were described in Chapter 2. Although it is easier to adjust for these factors when the cost is built up by elements, the lack of drawings at the program stage makes it a matter of guesswork allied to experience. It can often help, if no drawings are available, for the quantity surveyor to make a sketch plan of the building which would help to substantiate the basis for the estimate.

3. QUALITY

Adjustments for changes in quality are also easier to handle with an elemental breakdown. Because each element is priced individually it is comparatively easy to allow in the prices for differences in quality, and to explain to the client why and to what extent these adjustments have been made.

4. LOCATION

Costs will vary from location to location and if the proposed building is in one city while the only available cost analyses are for similar buildings in a different city an adjustment needs to be made. Publications which give index numbers between cities in North America include *Means Construction Cost Data* and the *Boeckh Building Valuation Manual*.

Also related to location is the type of soil on the site. It is unlikely that a soil report will be available at this stage but if there is any indication, such as known soil conditions on an adjoining site, that soil conditions differ from the analysis being used as the basis for the estimate an adjustment has to be made to `Foundations'.

5. INCLUSIONS AND EXCLUSIONS

The cost analyses on which the estimate is to be based should be checked to ensure that they are complete and that there are no exclusions. Partitions, finishes, fittings, fixtures and equipment in particular need to be verified and appropriate adjustments made if necessary. The analyses should include all the costs required for the estimate of the proposed building. At the same time they should not include more than is necessary.

Even though the foregoing adjustments have been made it is wise to add design and escalation allowances at the end of the estimate to cover unforeseen problems. An estimate prepared at this stage, although it may have been done with great care, cannot possibly foresee all the changes of mind and revisions which will take place between concept and the final contract documents, and a design allowance of ten per cent at this stage will give both the architects and the quantity surveyors room to manoeuvre. The estimate is always based on current prices and the percentage to allow for escalation will depend upon market conditions and the estimated time when tenders will be received. These allowances are dealt with in more detail later in this chapter.

At the completion of the program stage the first estimate can be presented for the client's approval and acceptance. It should be an honest attempt to show what the building might cost, based on all the available facts, and should not be influenced by the client's (or anyone else's) uninformed opinions about costs. Infinite trouble can develop later if the estimate is reduced because it is believed that a lower estimate will be more acceptable to the client, and it is patently dishonest if the reduction is made with the intention of selling the project to a potential client. Accompanying the estimate should be a brief description of what it does and does not include. This not only provides the client with needed information but also serves as useful documentation in the later stages of design. When the client has accepted this estimate it becomes the preliminary cost plan for the project, to be referred to in the next stage of the design process.

SCHEMATICS STAGE

Following the program stage is the schematics stage when the architects and their engineers will start consideration of the overall design of the building with the production of preliminary sketch drawings and an outline specification. If an estimate of cost was not asked for during the program stage it will certainly be requested now, and because more information is becoming available the accuracy of the estimate can be more certain. During this stage the architects will produce sketch drawings which show the basic size and shape of the building from which exterior wall, floor and roof areas can be measured, together with a specification which outlines the general standard of quality. The structural engineers will give some thought to the structural system they intend to use, and the mechanical and electrical engineers will do the same for their systems. The information will not be very detailed, but at least it is more than was available at the program stage.

This information does not become available in one neatly prepared package, but usually in a constantly flowing stream throughout the duration of the schematics stage. Floors can be added or removed, the shape can change and the interior planning amended, with revisions frequently being made to the specifications. Out of this welter of activity should come one or more schemes which need to be costed and compared with the cost plan, if there was one, prepared during the program stage.

The estimates during the schematics stage must be prepared in close collaboration with the architects, their engineers, and any other consultants. It helps, too, to have the client involved, and all must take some responsibility for their completeness.

Figure 7 shows an example of an estimate or cost plan for a district library using much of the information contained in the cost analysis shown in Figure 5. Although it is shown in metric the same format can be used for a building designed in imperial. As noted in the last chapter the cost plan format can be a much reduced version of the cost analysis format, generally showing costs only to the level of the elements, not to the sub-elements, unless there is a particular reason (and the information is available) to identify the cost of a sub-element. This means that, while cost analyses have a rigid format, a cost plan can have a more flexible format, tailored to the building being costed.

Depending on the amount of information available, the following is an outline of the approach which might be adopted for a cost plan:

1. SUBSTRUCTURE

It is highly unlikely that the structural engineers will have designed the foundations at this stage. The only way of estimating `Foundations' will be by measuring the area of the "footprint" of the building and using cost analyses of buildings which have the same number of storeys, making an adjustment if it is believed that the

Cost Plan

Project: Proposed District Library				Project No. 93250
Gross Floor Area: 3,126 m²	Architect: James Spinlove			Date: June 1993

Element	Ratio	Quantity	Unit Rate	Amount	Cost per m² Gross	Amount
A SHELL						
A1 Substructure						
A11 Foundations	0.54	1,692 m²	148.00	250,400	80.10	
A12 Basement Excavation	–	–	–	–	–	$80.10	$250,400
A2 Structure						
A21 Lowest Floor Construction	0.54	1,692 m²	51.70	87,500	27.99	
A22 Upper Floor Construction	0.46	1,434 m²	190.00	272,500	87.17	
A23 Roof Construction	0.54	1,692 m²	161.00	272,400	87.14	$202.30	$632,400
A3 Exterior Enclosure						
A31 Walls Below Grade	–	–	–	–	–	
A32 Walls Above Grade	0.58	1,815 m²	249.75	453,300	145.01	
A33 Windows & Entrances	0.09	280 m²	380.00	106,400	34.04	
A34 Roof Covering	0.54	1,692 m²	140.00	236,900	75.78	
A35 Projections				6,000	1.92	$256.75	$802,600
B INTERIORS						
B1 Partitions & Doors						
B11 Partitions	0.76	2,380 m²	85.20	201,800	64.88	
B12 Doors	0.04	126 m²	315.00	39,700	12.70	$77.58	$242,500
B2 Finishes						
B21 Floor Finishes	0.93	2,905 m²	66.40	192,900	61.71	
B22 Ceiling Finishes	0.93	2,905 m²	57.65	167,500	53.58	
B23 Wall Finishes	1.33	4,170 m²	26.45	110,300	35.28	$150.48	$470,400
B3 Fittings & Equipment						
B31 Fittings & Equipment				72,000	23.03	
B32 Equipment				–	–	
B33 Conveying Systems		1 No.		84,000	26.87	$49.90	$156,000
C Services						
C1 Mechanical						
C11 Plumbing & Drainage				98,800	31.61	
C12 Fire Protection				59,300	18.97	
C13 HVAC				355,600	113.76	
C14 Controls				39,500	12.64	$176.97	$553,200
C2 Electrical						
C21 Services & Distribution				62,800	20.09	
C22 Lighting, Devices & Heating				188,700	60.36	
Carried Forward				251,500	80.45	$994.08	$3,107,500

Figure 7

Element	Ratio	Quantity	Unit Rate	Amount	Cost per m² Gross		Amount
Brought Forward				251,500	80.45	$994.08	$3,107,500
C2 Electrical (continued)							
C23 Systems & Ancillaries				76,700	24.54	$104.99	$328,200
D SITE & ANCILLARY WORK							
D1 Site Work							
D11 Site Development		9,778 m²	22.50	220,000	70.38		
D12 Mechanical Site Services				46,000	14.72		
D13 Electrical Site Services				40,000	12.80	$97.89	$306,000
D2 Ancillary Work							
D21 Demolition				–	–		
D22 Alterations				–	–	–	–
Z General Requirements & Allowances							
Z1 General Requirements & Fee						$119.71	$374,200
Z2 Allowances							
Z21 Design Allowance				205,800	65.83		
Z22 Escalation Allowance				–	–		
Z23 Construction Allowance				–	–	$65.83	205,800
Total						$1,382.50	$4,321,700

Project: Proposed District Library — Project No. 93250
Gross Floor Area: 3,126 m² — Date: June 1993

Notes:
Based on Sketch Drawings SK1 - SK5.

Figure 7 (Concluded)

53

soil conditions may be different. If it is thought that there may be difficulties with the site an allowance for them can be made under `Special Foundations'.

`Basement Excavation' can be measured either as a cube as described in *Elemental Cost Analysis – Method of Measurement and Pricing*, or the actual quantities of excavation and backfill can be measured and priced separately.

2. STRUCTURE

Like `Foundations', `Lowest Floor Construction' is the footprint of the building and is measured as part of the gross floor area.

`Upper Floor Construction' is also measured as part of the gross floor area and should be the total gross floor area less the area of the `Lowest Floor Construction'. `Roof Construction' is usually the same area as the `Lowest Floor Construction' unless the building is expected to have roof overhangs. The structural engineers should be consulted about the type of construction, and how it may vary in the different parts of the building. They are usually very helpful in giving information on the probable type of structural system and the possible mass of structural steel or reinforcing steel per square metre or square foot of the structure, the column spacings, and the thickness and types of floor and roof slabs. Rather than relying on cost analyses for the costs of these two elements it is frequently better to work out the cost of typical bays from the information provided by the structural engineers as was described in Chapter 3 and to check the results with cost analyses of similar structures to see whether they look reasonable.

3. EXTERIOR ENCLOSURE

Most of the elements in this group can usually be measured from the sketch drawings, although it will probably be necessary to work out the areas of `Windows & Entrances' as a percentage of the total exterior cladding. This is not difficult to do if percentages of windows, glazed screens and doors have been recorded with the analyses of past projects as described in the last chapter. The architects may have some idea of what they propose to use for exterior cladding, or they may only have a general idea of the standard of quality. In the former case it is possible to build up unit rates for each type of cladding, but if they only have an idea of the standard of quality they are looking for, reference would have to be made to cost analyses and unit rates corresponding to the standard of quality they have in mind. In either case the intent is not to restrict the architects to any particular material or cladding system, but only to ensure that a reasonable amount of money has been allocated to each of the elements to allow them some flexibility in the later design stages.

The only element which it may not be possible to measure is `Projections'. They may not be shown on the drawings, but the architects may be able to indicate whether they expect any, and if so what the projections are likely to be, in which case they can either be measured or included as lump sum allowances.

4. PARTITIONS & DOORS

Partitions and doors are not usually shown on the drawings at this stage, or only some of them are shown, or the partitions are shown without the doors, and in any case the types of partitions have not yet been decided. The best solution is to use the ratios from cost analyses of similar building types to give quantities for the partitions and doors. Even if some of the partitions are shown there is no point in measuring them because it still leaves the remainder to be guessed at. If the drawings have advanced enough for all the partitions and doors to be shown they can be measured and the ratios used to check that the quantities look reasonable. Pricing of partitions and doors, because they can be such a mixture of different materials, is best done by using the unit rates in cost analyses of similar building types.

5. FINISHES

Measurement of Finishes when a detailed estimate is being prepared is always time-consuming and out of all proportion to their value in the total building cost. At the Schematics stage the gross floor area, with an adjustment to reduce it to a net finished area, can be used to provide an area for `Floor Finishes' and `Ceiling Finishes' since these elements relate directly to the floor area. The adjustment to be used would be the ratio shown for these elements in the cost analysis for a similar type of building.

`Wall Finishes' cannot be measured at this stage but they can be calculated by taking the area of `Walls Below Grade' plus the area of `Walls Above Grade' plus twice times the area of `Partitions & Doors' and applying a ratio to the result as described in the last chapter to give an approximate quantity of wall finishes.

Unit rates from cost analyses can be used to price the finishes or, if the architects have given some thought to the finishes they will use, the quantities can be sub-divided by percentages of types of finish. For example, the architects may consider that the floor finishes are likely to be 60% carpet, 10% mosaic floor tile, 25% resilient flooring, and 5% exposed concrete. Applying these percentages to the net finished area enables a price to be calculated separately for each type of applied finish.

6. FITTINGS & EQUIPMENT

It is unlikely that the architects have given much thought to this group of elements, except perhaps for `Conveying Systems', at such an early stage, and quantities cannot be measured. The estimate must therefore be based on lump sum allowances or costs per square unit of the gross floor area obtained from cost analyses, with adjustments for any known items of fittings, furnishings or equipment.

`Conveying Systems' can be costed by pricing the number of each type. A rule of thumb for calculating the number of elevators is to allow one passenger elevator for every 500-750 people who will occupy the building and one freight elevator for every three passenger elevators or for every 7,000 m² of net floor area.[1]

7. SERVICES

The designs of the mechanical and electrical services tend to follow a long way behind the architectural design. Normally it is not be possible to measure quantities for `Services' at this stage, so the estimate has to be done on the basis of square metre or square foot costs. It is advisable to review the estimate for the services with the engineers before incorporating it into the cost plan.

8. SITE & ANCILLARY WORK

If any of the site development is shown it can be measured and priced as described in *Elemental Cost Analysis – Method of Measurement and Pricing*, otherwise it should be priced as an overall cost per square metre or square foot of the site. The cost of site development rarely has any relationship to the cost of the building and the size of the building cannot therefore be used to calculate it. Mechanical and Electrical site services usually have to be included as lump sum amounts and, as with `Services', they should be reviewed with the engineers. `Site Work' is rather a flexible element since its cost can be expanded and contracted, within limits, without affecting the quality of the building.

`Demolition' and `Alterations' if they occur usually have to be included as lump sum estimates at this stage.

---

[1] For more precise calculations to determine the number of elevators see *Project Budgeting for Buildings* by Parker and Dell'Isola.

9. GENERAL REQUIREMENTS & ALLOWANCES

`General Requirements & Fee' can be included as a percentage of the total construction cost at this stage. Reference to cost analyses will give an indication of the percentage to use, although it is usually safe to allow 10%.

`Allowances' used to be known as `Contingencies'. A design allowance is essential to give the architects and their engineers some flexibility in their decisions during the later design stages. The amount will depend on the type and complexity of the building and the degree of confidence the design team has in the cost plan. As noted earlier, an allowance of 10% of the total estimated cost would not be unreasonable.

An escalation allowance may or may not be included, some clients preferring to use their own crystal ball. The amount will depend on current market conditions and how long it will be before tenders are likely to be called.

A cost plan is intended to predict costs when tenders are called. Consequently a construction allowance, which is intended to allow for changes in cost during construction, is not usually needed. If this allowance is included, it needs to be deducted before the cost plan is compared with the tenders. If it is not included, the client should include an allowance of about 3% in the overall project budget.

Some clients like to have the building cost separated from the site development cost. In this case it will be necessary to present two cost plans, one showing costs against all groups except `Site & Ancillary Work', and the other with costs shown only against `Site & Ancillary Work' and `General Requirements & Allowances'. The costs for `General Requirements & Allowances' would have to be proportioned between the building and the site development. A third cost plan could show the consolidated costs for the whole project.

In the last chapter it was mentioned that unit rates can be kept up to date by calculating quantities for each of the element areas. This can also be done for a cost plan, but it is not recommended. By multiplying the element area by the unit quantity a schedule of quantities can be concocted for the cost plan. For example, in the last chapter it was found that for every square metre of `Foundations' there was 1.6208 m^3 of excavation. With a new area of 1,692 m^2 this means that a total of 2,742 m^3 (1,692 x 1.6208) of excavation has been included in the cost plan shown in Figure 7. This looks very impressive but can give a client the mistaken impression that the quantities have, in fact, been measured and that the cost plan is the result of a detailed estimate. Not only is this misleading since the quantities are obviously false, intended only to impress a client, but it goes against the whole concept of cost planning as it was described earlier in this chapter by trying to identify materials within the elements.

It is unusual for only one cost plan to have to be prepared during this stage. Often two or more are required to see the cost effect of alternative design solutions or because the client wants changes to be made. By the end of the schematics stage all the fundamental decisions, certainly those concerning cost, have been made. Although decisions on details still have to be made, the size, shape, height, type of construction and general standard of quality will have been established and these key decisions will have determined the basic cost of the building. All the important decisions regarding cost are made by the end of the schematics stage, not at some later stage in the design and, unless a major change is made in the scope of the project, all future decisions will have comparatively minor effects on the cost.

As the cost plan is being developed questions should be raised about whether components are making the best contribution to the building, whether there is a better way of incorporating them, or whether they need to be there at all. Besides giving an indication of the anticipated cost, the cost plan should be used to review the balance of costs over the elements to ensure that the building owners are obtaining value for money. If the cost plan indicates an over-expenditure in any element it should be pointed out to the architects to give them the opportunity to justify the expenditure, or to make adjustments to their design to bring the costs back into balance.

At the end of the schematics stage the cost plan is presented together with the schematic drawings. It may be a new plan, or it may be an updating of the preliminary cost plan done at the program stage. It is an interpretation in costs of all the key decisions which have been made by the architects, their engineers, and the client in a form which shows how it is intended to spend the money on each of the elements in the building. If it is followed properly it can be used to control costs as the design is further developed.

Because it is going to be used as a working tool, the presentation of the cost plan is important. It should be accompanied by a description of what has and has not been included, together with any quantities and unit prices which have been measured or assumed to establish it. Each member of the design team should be given a copy of the documentation so that they know the parameters within which they will be working as the design progresses, and how those parameters were established. Since the architects and their engineers should have played a major role in setting the parameters there should be no difficulty in accepting them and at the conclusion of the schematics stage there should be a basic design coupled with a cost plan, both of which are acceptable to the client, the architects and their engineers.

CHAPTER 6

Cost Control

Once the cost plan has been accepted at the end of the schematics stage it will be used to help control costs during the balance of the pre-tender period. Cost control requires the understanding and co-operation of the architects and their engineers. If they do not fully understand and accept it, decisions can be made without reference to the cost plan and the time spent in preparing the plan will have been wasted.

The essence of any cost control program is to have a frame of reference, followed by a means of checking, and finally a means of taking remedial action if costs are found to be getting out of control. In this instance the cost plan is the frame of reference. It shows the total amount of money to be spent and how it is to be distributed over the elements of the building, setting up cost targets for each of them. The means of checking is to carry out cost checks during the design development and contract documents stages, and the remedial action is taken by all members of the design team when problems become apparent.

Cost control is carried out during the final two stages of the design process and, although they are described here as separate stages, the distinction between them can often become blurred.

DESIGN DEVELOPMENT STAGE

During the design development stage the architects and their engineers will consider the detailed design of all the components of the building. The element `Walls Above Grade' can be used to illustrate how the cost plan is used to help control cost during this stage.

At the schematics stage it is possible that no firm decision was made on the type of exterior wall to be used, only a broad assumption that perhaps some form of precast cladding of a certain quality might be considered. Although the cost plan would not identify the materials to be used, it would set a cost target for the element based on this general standard of quality. Now, at the design development stage, a firm decision has to be made on the cladding. The architects may already have decided which cladding system they wish to use and will prepare preliminary design drawings and an outline specification for it. Or they may wish to consider several different design solutions before making a final decision, in which case they would provide drawings and outline specifications for each of them. Each design option proposed by the architects, whether there is only one or several of them, can then be costed using the unit in place method and compared with the cost plan. This is the means of checking mentioned above.

If only one design is being considered it may be found to exceed the cost target set for the element, and if several alternatives are being considered some may be more acceptable to the architects but be too expensive, while others may meet the budget but be less acceptable as a design solution. The ideal would be a design which the architects find acceptable and which is within the cost target for the element. If the design the architects would like to use exceeds the cost target, three courses of action are available to them:

1. They can accept the higher figure and make a compensating reduction in one or more of the other elements to cover the difference. They may already have found savings in other elements, in which case money could be made available from them. If this is not possible, or if the savings they have found are not enough, the element `Design Allowance' can be used as a source of additional money provided it hasn't already been used for other elements and still contains sufficient funds. If this option is available it will mean that the distribution of costs in the cost plan will be modified, but the total estimated cost will be unchanged.

2. They can resign themselves to accepting a less desirable architectural solution to stay within budget. Although this may not be entirely satisfactory to the architects, it will be the only available option if the other two are impracticable or unacceptable.

3.   The client can be asked for additional money to cover the extra cost. The architects would have to give an explanation for the request to their client, which is easier when reference can be made to the cost plan. It is the least desirable course of action and, although the client will have been warned about the budget deficiency reasonably early in the design process rather than when tenders are opened, it is unlikely to be a satisfactory solution from the client's standpoint, and should only be considered in exceptional circumstances. The one occasion when this should be acceptable is when the increase is due the client's request for additional requirements.

Accepting one of these three options is the remedial action mentioned earlier.

All the elements are considered within this context until an acceptable solution is found for each of them in a sequence of:

1. Design of the element
2. Costing of the element
3. Comparison with the cost plan
4. Decision and action on the design

Each architectural firm has its own way of working and quantity surveyors are rarely presented with a set of drawings and draft specifications for a single element and asked to cost them for comparison with the cost plan quite as described above. Instead, at various stages throughout design development they will usually receive a set of partially completed working drawings and specifications which, when completed, will become the contract documents. These may be accompanied by design sketches which will be used by the draughtsman or computer operator to complete the working drawings. The quantity surveyors will be asked to update their estimate from this information using the unit in place method when possible and, since the updated estimate will be prepared in the same elemental format as the cost plan, most of the elements will be checked and remedial action taken on those elements which require it. The procedures will therefore be the same but the elements will be dealt with as a whole rather than singly.

It can be useful to have a standard form to record the cost checks on the elements as they are done. It would give a description of the check and show the element's original cost target, its current cost if a previous cost check had revised the target, its new cost and which other elements, if any, are affected. If the new cost is accepted the amount would be entered on a Cost Summary which keeps track of the status of the project. Examples of these forms are shown in Appendix C.

At the end of the design development stage, designs of all the elements should have been completed and shown on the preliminary working drawings, and the cost of each element should have been tested against its cost target. There may have been some redistribution of the costs over the elements, but provided the cost plan was adequate, unless the owner has increased the scope the overall budget should be unchanged or may even be reduced.

CONTRACT DOCUMENT STAGE

The final stage of the design process is the contract document stage when the decisions made during design development are translated into final working drawings and specifications. As there is a tendency for these two stages to overlap the work at this stage is really a continuation and finalization of the work done during design development. If a complete estimate was not done toward the end of design development it is advisable to make one using the unit in place method early in the contract document stage to ensure that a decision taken on one element has not affected the cost of another element and gone unnoticed.

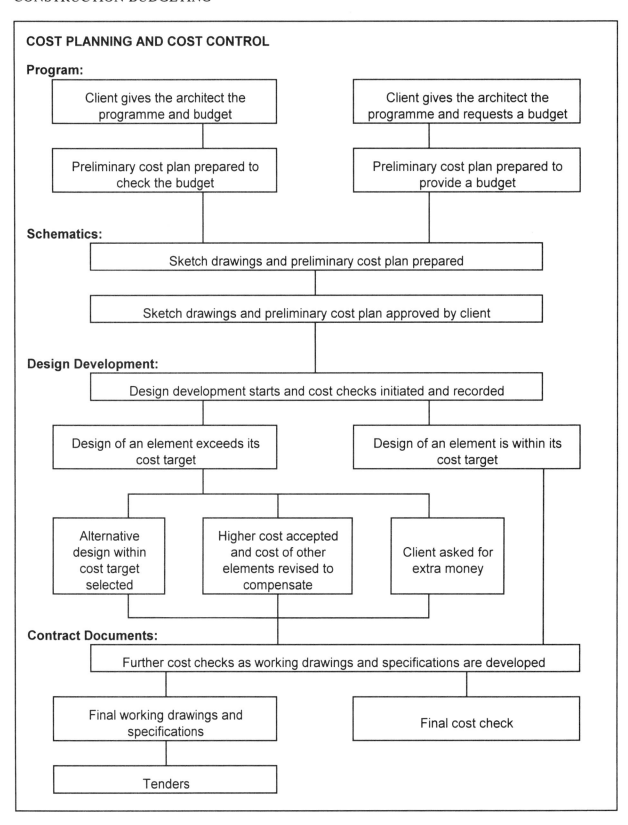

Figure 8

A further estimate, also using the unit in place method, when the working drawings are about 80-90% complete should be done to make sure that no additional cost items have manifested themselves while the working drawings and specifications are being finalized. This estimate should be done on an elemental breakdown and is really a final check of the cost plan. It can be used as the basis for a cost analysis for help with future projects, but should also be re-analyzed as a trade breakdown so a comparison can be made between the estimate and the breakdown submitted by the successful contractor. This serves two purposes: it helps ensure that the successful contractor's breakdown is reasonably accurate, and it can show where discrepancies exist between the estimate and the tender so that the elemental cost analysis can be adjusted, if necessary, to make it reflect the actual tender more accurately.

In the case of a management or fast-track contract the same basic sequence of events takes place, the principal difference being that the trade breakdown is prepared earlier on. An elemental cost plan is still required at the end of the schematics stage as an aid to the design team, but the trade breakdown is started shortly thereafter and becomes the cost plan for construction. As tenders are called and checked against the construction cost plan, adjustments may have to be made to the design to bring expenditure back within the budget. Although a management contractor is brought in at an early stage some management contractors have experience only of costs in the general contractors' trades and for this reason, and for reasons of continuity, it is preferable to have whoever prepared the original cost plan continue with the cost control until all tenders have been received and the final costs known.

Figure 8 shows the cost planning and cost control process in chart form. It should be made clear that it is not intended to produce cheap buildings, nor is it intended to inhibit design. The aim is to ensure that from the outset building owners' budgets are adequate for the types of buildings they are proposing, that they get value for money, and that there are no unpleasant shocks when tenders are opened. The architects in the meantime are kept informed of the cost effects of all their decisions and given adequate warning if costs are running high, before the design has advanced to a stage where it is difficult, and expensive, for them to change it. Too often in the past the inadequacy of the budget became evident only when tenders were opened and the options mentioned in Chapter 1 had to be considered. As for inhibiting design, there is nothing more inhibiting to a design than an inadequate budget and a lack of knowledge of the cost implications of design decisions.

A cost control program can only work if all members of the design team – the project manager, the architects, their engineers, the quantity surveyors, any other consultants, and the building owner – not only understand it but are fully committed to it and take full responsibility for making it work. Only then, with the architects and their consultants organizing their information to co-ordinate with the cost plan, with everyone accepting the reliability of the costs and recognizing that cost control is the responsibility of the whole team, can cost control succeed.

At the same time, it is important to keep the subject in perspective. Estimating, cost planning and cost control are exercises in forecasting and forecasting the future, as any weatherman knows, can produce accurate results only as long as it isn't done more than six hours ahead. Building owners frequently ask how close the tenders should be to the final cost plan. Since a spread of ten per cent between bidders when they are all based on the same sub-trade bids is not unusual, a similar spread between the cost plan and the low tender should be acceptable. However, even when the design team can call on a substantial body of past experience, and can capably assess current trends, there is no way the results can be guaranteed. Most often the results are satisfactory, but sometimes through unforeseen circumstances tenders can be higher than predicted. One consolation then is that it might have been considerably worse if no attempt had been made to plan and control the costs.

PART 2

Economics of Development

CHAPTER 7

Feasibility Studies

In the past many real estate developments were carried out by developers with little more than a feeling for a particular site and the drive and endurance to push the project through to completion with a minimum of their own money and very little professional advice. Sometimes the economic viability of the development was justified with a page or two of calculations based on questionable facts provided by people who had a vested interest in seeing the project started. More often than not the developers had no idea of what their real costs were until some time after the development was completed. Inevitably any correlation between the final cost and the developers' original calculations was purely coincidental and the reason some of their projects turned out to be successful was that inflation took care of their mistakes.

In recent years the emergence of a more sophisticated developer, the large size of some of the urban developments recently being undertaken and the requirements of the lending institutions has meant that the days of the developer who does not make a thorough preliminary study are over. A fully comprehensive feasibility study can require the combined talents of many people including architects, engineers, space planners, market analysts, appraisers, realtors, traffic consultants, lawyers, accountants, money managers, builders, quantity surveyors, sociologists, economists, environmentalists and ecologists.

Stated in its simplest terms there are two criteria by which the feasibility or economic merit of a development will be judged. These are the two factors mentioned in Chapter 1, cost and value, and it is the relationship between them which is analyzed in a feasibility study.

Three techniques are available to an appraiser when measuring the value of real estate. The first, which is generally considered to be the most reliable, is the market value approach. Comparable properties in the vicinity which have recently been sold are investigated by the appraiser to help assess how much might be paid by a potential purchaser for the property being appraised. Since no two properties are identical the appraiser would have to make adjustments to allow for differences but the outcome should be a reasonably close assessment of the value.

If no properties in the vicinity have recently been sold and this approach cannot be used, or if the appraiser wants to confirm the appraisal, the second method known as the cost approach can be used. This requires an estimate of the cost to replace the building at current prices, frequently done by a quantity surveyor, together with a valuation, possibly using the market value approach, for the land. If the building is not new a deduction depending upon the age of the building and its components has to be made for depreciation.

The third technique is the income approach where the value is based on the income which can be generated by the property over its life. The income is discounted to give its present value using the formulae described in Chapter 9.

While a feasibility study attempts to show that the value of a real estate development at least equals its cost, not all building owners concern themselves with the economic facts alone. An institutional owner may be more concerned with the design of the building as a prestige symbol, conferring indirect benefits far beyond those which an analysis shows is its pure economic worth. The concern then is not for a building which has the highest value in terms of making money, but for a building which has the highest value as a prestige symbol, while at the same time losing the least amount of money.

Although feasibility studies are usually thought of in the context of new construction they can also be applied to alterations and additions to existing buildings, or to determine whether old buildings should be renovated or demolished. When a building owner is considering enlarging an existing building, a feasibility study should be made on the before and after values of the property to see whether the cost of the addition makes economic sense. Similarly, a feasibility study can assist a building owner in deciding whether to renovate an existing building or to demolish it and rebuild. These studies could take the form of a life-cycle cost analysis, which will be described in Chapter 12, and might show that the income in either case would be less than could be earned by selling the site and investing the proceeds of the sale in some other form of investment.

In most circumstances a feasibility study is directed toward providing investors with a measure of confidence in the probable economic results of investing their money in a real estate development. In other words, whether they will receive a good return on their investment. The type of real estate of interest to such investors would be self-sustaining, revenue-producing properties such as office buildings, apartment buildings, shopping centres, medical centres, industrial buildings, and, in some instances, housing developments.

A feasibility study requires a collection of all the facts – the need for the project, its capital cost, its income, and its operating costs – which have to be analyzed to test its viability.

MARKET STUDIES

The first step in the preparation of a feasibility study for a project which is to be leased or sold is a market study to determine whether there is a demand for the type of property the developer intends to build. This is quite a critical stage since an improperly conducted market study can seriously affect the viability of the project. If there is an obvious demand the study may be done by the developer, but for a project of any size it is usual to enlist the services of a consulting firm specializing in this type of work. No matter who is responsible for the study it is important to remember that merely knowing there is a shortage of a particular type of accommodation does not in itself constitute a demand: it has to be accompanied by a willingness on the part of a purchaser to buy, or potential tenants to pay rents, at levels which make the development economically viable. Demand signifies only that which can be paid for.

The market study would cover such matters as:

1. The amount of comparable accommodation presently available and, in the case of rental properties, the extent to which they are being rented, and whether the vacancy rate is high.
2. Whether there might be competition for the development from any other new projects being contemplated.
3. The rate at which demand for new space has been satisfied in recent years, and the probable demand in the future based on possible business expansion and economic growth.
4. For a rental property, the prevailing rents in the area, together with an assessment of local leasing practices with regard to escalation, renewals, length of term, etc.
5. An assessment of transportation facilities in the area.
6. Any other factors which might have a bearing on the economic feasibility of the development.

The market study will provide essential information upon which the developer can make initial decisions. The research may indicate that the development might be enlarged or reduced in size, developed in stages, revised in concept, postponed, or abandoned altogether – decisions which it is wise to make as early as possible in the development process.

CAPITAL COSTS

If the market study indicates that the development might be viable, the next step is to assemble the capital costs which will be required to complete the project. Capital costs are usually referred to as either hard costs or soft costs. Soft costs are also sometimes called development costs. Hard costs would include:

1. LAND

This would include not only the actual cost of the land but also real estate commissions, title insurance and land transfer taxes. Where the developer has owned the land for some time it should be appraised at its current market value and this amount used. If the land is leased, its present value based on the income it can generate can be used.

2. DEMOLITION

If existing buildings have to be demolished, or even if only a tree is to be removed, these costs have to be included. Demolition costs are frequently included in the construction cost, but sometimes demolition is a separate contract preceding the construction contract, in which case it has to be included separately.

3. CONSTRUCTION

This is the largest single hard cost and it is therefore important that it should be as accurate as possible. Most developers include in this category only the actual cost of construction, while others include architects' and other consultants' fees.

Soft, or development, costs would include:

1. LAND SURVEYS

Two surveys are usually conducted, one prior to construction and another when the development is finished. These are required for both construction and mortgage purposes.

2. SOIL TESTS

Unless the type of soil is already known, a soil test will be required to enable the structural engineer to design appropriate foundations. In a major urban centre this would probably also include an environmental analysis to check the amount and types of contaminated soil, if any.

3. MARKET STUDIES

These have been described in the previous section of this chapter.

4. APPRAISAL FEES

This would include the fees for the mortgage company's appraisal as well as an appraisal which may be required by the developer.

5. DESIGN FEES

As noted earlier, some developers include architects' and other design consultants' fees in the hard costs.

6. SPECIAL CONSULTANTS' FEES

These cover specialized professional consultants such as traffic consultants, acoustic consultants and any other consultants whose fees are not included elsewhere.

7. LEGAL FEES

These would include fees in connection with the purchase of the land, incorporating a property company to handle the development, mortgage company's legal costs, developer's mortgage legal costs, interim lender's legal costs, land transfer charges, re-zoning applications, and drafting leases, trust deeds, and bond purchase agreements, etc.

8. ACCOUNTING FEES

If a property company is to be incorporated to handle the development an accounting firm may be needed to audit the books during construction.

9. UNDERWRITER'S FEES

If the money for the development is to be raised by means of a bond issue the underwriters will require a fee.

10. DEVELOPER'S FEE

The developer may require a fee over and above any return made on the investment in the property.

11. PROJECT MANAGEMENT FEE

A project management firm may be employed to manage the development on behalf of the developer.

12. FURNISHINGS

This may be quite minimal on some developments. It would include loose furniture, sun drapes, carpeting and any other items needed to make the building habitable, and which have not been included in the construction cost.

13. ART WORK

If this has not been included in the construction cost it should be allowed for as a soft cost.

14. MUNICIPAL LEVIES

These are capital levies imposed by some municipalities on new developments as a contribution toward municipal services such as sewers, etc.

15. PARKING LEVIES

If the development does not provide sufficient parking space the municipality may levy a charge to help defray the cost of public parking.

16. CAPITAL TAXES

Some provincial governments levy a tax on paid up capital stock, retained earnings, loans, etc. of incorporated companies. Provision should be made for this if a property company is to be incorporated to handle the development.

17. REAL ESTATE TAXES

These are levied on the land before construction and on the development during construction. An improvement tax during construction may be levied on a phased development where part of the development is to be handed over and occupied prior to general completion.

18. INSURANCE

On new construction the general contractor is usually required to take out an all-risks insurance policy on the construction. If the development consists of renovations to an existing building the increased cost of the existing insurance policy during construction should be included as a soft cost.

19. MORTGAGE INSURANCE

This protects the mortgage company against the developer defaulting in the mortgage payments.

20. PERFORMANCE BONDS

These should be included as a soft cost if they have not been included in the construction cost.

21. INITIAL MAINTENANCE COSTS

Although the contractor may give a twelve-month warranty on its work and materials there is likely to be some maintenance work required between the completion of construction and the start of income from the development.

22. ACCOMMODATION

Space may have to be rented to accommodate the developer's staff and consultants such as the project manager.

23. DEVELOPER'S ADMINISTRATIVE COSTS

These may be included in the Developer's Fee (10) and Accommodation (22) but if they aren't, such items as salaries, heat, light, telephone, travel, and other administrative expenses should be included here.

24. LEASING COMMISSIONS

A development company may sometimes arrange its own leasing for the building and include the cost in its administrative costs, but if a real estate firm is brought in as the leasing agent, fees will have to be paid for this service, usually based on a percentage of the rental income.

25. ADVERTISING AND PUBLIC RELATIONS

Any project in which it is intended to rent space or which is intended to be sold will require an advertising budget to attract tenants or buyers.

26. TENANT INDUCEMENTS

As an enticement to potential tenants in a commercial development the developer will frequently offer an allowance of a certain amount per square metre or per square foot toward the cost of tenant partitions and finishes. The developer may also offer free rent for a period of time.

27. TENANT LEASE TAKEOVERS

As a further inducement to a potential tenant the developer may agree to take over an existing lease if the tenant moves into the new building.

28. INTERIM FINANCE

This is sometimes known as bridging financing and is a short term loan from a bank or trust company to cover construction and other costs until the permanent financing becomes available. Since permanent financing is not usually provided until the construction is complete, and since interim financing has a higher rate of interest, the amount which is included here depends to a large extent on the efficiency and speed of the design and construction teams. A long delay in construction or a major increase in construction cost can add considerably to the cost of interim financing.

29. INTERIM LENDER COMMITMENT FEES

An interim lender will normally require a commitment fee from the developer when the loan agreement is signed.

30. LONG-TERM LENDER STANDBY FEES

This is similar to the previous item but would be levied by the mortgage company on the mortgage loan.

31. BROKERAGE COMMISSION

This is a finder's fee paid by the developer to an agent for being introduced to sources of money, both short and long term.

32. REGISTRATION FEES

If money is to be raised by means of debentures, the charge for registering them has to be included.

33. INITIAL OCCUPANCY COSTS

These are initial costs incurred between the completion of construction and the occupancy of the building, such as the cost of training staff to operate the building.

34. CONTINGENCIES

This is an allowance to cover all unforeseen costs arising from items which may have been underestimated or overlooked in estimating the total capital cost.

35. INCOME DURING CONSTRUCTION

The feasibility study has to be based on figures current at a certain point in time, usually when construction is finished. If there is any likelihood that some income will be generated before construction is completed as, for example, in a phased development or where deposits are to be received from condominium buyers, this income should be totalled and deducted from the total capital cost.

This list does not include every possible capital expense, nor will all of them be applicable to every development, but it does provide a checklist for many of those which can be expected on any major development.

INCOME

Since a feasibility study is directed toward showing that the real estate value of a development is at least equal to its costs, the next step is to examine the value, for which the potential income and running expenses are required.

The sole source of income from an income-producing real estate development is the rentals which can be charged, and one of the tasks of the design consultants is to maximize this revenue. However, this objective should not override all other considerations. The attempt should be rather to achieve a proper balance between income and operating expenses, with due regard being paid to those features which contribute to the preservation of the investment on a long-term basis, not to mention those which contribute to the environment.

Where the feasibility study is being done for the purpose of deciding the worth of purchasing an existing revenue-producing property, the assessment of income is based on the existing revenue generated by the property and is therefore comparatively simple. Where it is for a proposed development the income has to be estimated. The market study should show the range of rents which might be expected, and it is then a matter of judgement on the part of the developer to use rental rates based on market conditions and the quality and cost of the building being constructed.

Rental rates vary with the type of building and the basis on which they are charged will also differ. The following gives a general idea of how some rentals are charged:

1. OFFICE BUILDINGS

The rental is based on the rentable floor area. The most usual method of measuring the rentable floor area is described in *Standard Method of Floor Measurement* published by Building Owners and Managers Association International, 224 Michigan Avenue, Chicago, Illinois 60604, U.S.A. Briefly, with a full-floor occupancy it is usually measured to the inside face of the exterior walls, with deductions for stairwells, elevator shafts, duct shafts and mechanical spaces only. If the tenant takes only a part of a floor the area is taken to the centre line of the demising partitions and the inside face of the exterior and corridor walls, with no deductions for columns. In this case, because the developer does not rent washrooms or corridors, the rental rate will be higher than on a full-floor occupancy. Normally the ground floor will rent at a higher rate than any other floor. The rental rate may be net, with the tenant paying taxes and certain operating costs separately or it may be fixed and all-inclusive. The lease may also contain an escalation clause. The variety of ways in which the rental rate can be established is limited only by the developer's imagination and the tenant's acquiescence.

2. APARTMENT BUILDINGS

The rental is on a per suite basis, varying according to the size and quality of the suite, and the availability of any supplementary facilities such as a health club or swimming pool.

3. FACTORIES

The rental is usually based on the gross floor area, measured to the outside face of the exterior walls, and the rate is usually on a net basis with the tenant paying for all operating costs, including taxes.

4. SHOPPING CENTRES

A shopping centre may contain office accommodation, theatres, restaurants and gas stations as well as retail and department stores, and the leasing arrangements will differ for each. A common arrangement, except for the office accommodation, is for the tenants to agree to a minimum rent based on the floor area, plus a percentage of their income based on audited receipts, which means the rent can vary considerably depending on the turnover.

OPERATING COSTS

Operating costs can be separated into two types: those which occur annually and those which occur periodically. They can further be subdivided into occupancy, or user, costs and ownership costs. Occupancy costs are those costs which are related to the activities which are being carried on within the building, such as the cost of medical staff in a hospital or the costs of running an assembly line in a factory. Ownership costs are those costs which occur whether the building is occupied or not. There may be occasions when both occupancy costs and ownership costs need to be separately identified, but for the purpose of a feasibility study only the ownership costs usually need to be considered.

Annual ownership operating costs would include:

1. Real estate taxes.
2. Insurance.

3. Cleaning and supplies. This may be done by the developer's own staff or by an outside cleaning organization.

4. Hydro.

5. Fuel.

6. Water.

7. Security.

8. Operating staff.

9. Service contracts. This would include the cost of annual contracts to maintain elevators, air conditioning equipment, etc.

10. Supplies. This would include light bulbs, cleaning supplies, stationery for the superintendent, etc.

11. Building Management. On large projects this is often handled by the developer's staff in which case it would be included in item 8. Alternatively a professional property management firm may be engaged to collect rents, investigate complaints and make periodic checks of the building. The property management firm may also arrange leasing.

12. Garbage Removal.

13. Snow Removal.

14. Gardening. This would include all outside staff for gardening, pool maintenance, etc.

15. Land rental.

16. Preventative maintenance.

17. Vacancy allowance. Very few buildings can be rented completely. If income has been calculated on the basis of a fully-rented building without allowance for vacancies, such an allowance should be made here in the annual operating costs.

18. Legal and audit. Legal and audit fees will be required, particularly if a property company has been formed, but in any case allowance should be made for preparing lease agreements.

19. External and internal communications equipment. This would include telephone, telex and internal communications systems.

20. Finance costs. This covers payment of interest on loans and will be dealt with in more detail in the next chapter.

Depending upon the terms of the lease some of these costs might be paid directly by the tenants but this provides a checklist of annual operating costs which can be expected on a major development.

Periodic ownership operating costs would include:

1. Periodic decoration of public areas.

2. Periodic Repairs.

3. Potential future alterations. If it is known that alterations will be made at some time in the future, their cost can be estimated and included here, but this is, in fact, a very unlikely item to appear in the feasibility study for a new development.

The assembly of all these facts to determine the viability of a project will be examined in Chapter 10.

CHAPTER 8

Financing

Developers rarely use their own money to finance their projects and financing is therefore a very important aspect of real estate development. If it is not considered carefully, what might at first sight appear to be an attractive investment could turn out to be a financial disaster.

Most construction projects need two forms of financing: interim financing used to help pay expenses during construction, and permanent financing, usually in the form of a mortgage, which comes into effect when construction is complete and the project starts to generate income.

INTERIM FINANCING

The amount of the loan developers need to enable them to start building their projects will depend on their financial resources. In some cases they may be able to provide the funds themselves but it is usual, except for the smallest of projects, for them to have to borrow the money.

Interim financing is usually provided by a bank or trust company and, because the loan is not backed by a completed building as it is with a mortgage, the interest rate is higher than it will be for the mortgage.

Before it will consider a loan the lender will require a pro-forma budget from the developer showing the estimated capital costs to assure itself that the development is viable. When the lender is satisfied that the project can be built within the developer's budget and has at least a reasonable chance of being successful, it will enter into a loan agreement with the developer. The agreement will state the maximum amount of the loan, the commitment fee, the time period over which the money will be borrowed and the rate of interest, together with any other requirements which the lender may have. The interest rate is usually stated as a certain percentage above prime and since the prime rate can vary from time to time the rate can also vary over the period of the loan.

Once the loan is in place the borrower makes an application each month for an advance and, provided it is approved by the lender, money is advanced to pay that month's expenses. Interest is charged at the current rate each month on the total, including accrued interest, drawn down to date.

Lenders always require the developer to have some equity in the project, often the value of the land, and will not start advancing money until the developer's equity has been exhausted. This helps protect the lender in the event that the development starts running into difficulties, since the borrower will already have a sizable investment in the project. Also as a form of protection the lender always advances money on a cost to complete basis. Each month it will review the borrower's application and will advance only so much of the loan as will ensure that there is sufficient money left to complete the project in the event that the developer defaults. This can mean that the borrower may sometimes have to increase its equity. If a cost overrun becomes apparent and the cost to complete increases, the lender will reduce the amount of the advance, leaving the borrower to find the additional funds to cover its costs for that month.

To estimate the cost of interim financing properly a cash flow is required, showing how expenditures will accumulate month by month. Interest can then be estimated by assuming an interest rate for each month and totalling each month's interest to give a total cost for the project.

Several quantity surveying firms now act as consultants to financial institutions in monitoring these short-term loans. This work is very specialized and requires a good knowledge of finance and banking as well as construction costs and unless it is competently done it can expose the quantity surveyor to claims and litigation.

The interim lender is particularly concerned about the developer's arrangements for permanent financing since it is only when this is in place that the loan will be repaid. Sometimes the interim lender will also provide the permanent financing, but more often the permanent financing is provided by another financial institution.

PERMANENT FINANCING

As with interim financing, the first consideration in permanent financing is the size of the loan. If the developer wishes to invest a minimum amount of money in the development a loan will have to be arranged and as a result the developer may have to accept a lower yield on the investment because part of the income will have to be used to pay off the loan. On the other hand, financing a project with its own money may lose some of the leverage which can be provided by borrowing money. Usually it is advisable to borrow some of the money for a development, but this is not always necessarily the case. If the development is a comparatively modest undertaking, such as a small industrial building with a first-class tenant, it may be better for the developer, if it has the money available, to invest it in the development rather than to take out a loan.

If the developer decides it needs to borrow money the next consideration is how it will be borrowed. The most common way of doing so is to take out a mortgage on the property, but there are other ways. Many major buildings have been financed by mortgage bonds which are sold to the general public through investment dealers and mortgage brokers. If mortgage bonds are to be issued, one of the chief requirements is that the development should be backed by top-class tenants. If an investor is thinking of buying, say, General Motors bonds at 6.5% and is offered mortgage bonds at 8.5% for a building in which General Motors will be the prime tenant, the investor would be wise to take the mortgage bonds since they offer an extra 2% and are, in effect, backed by the same company. Another alternative to a mortgage is to offer shares in a property company which is to be formed to carry out the development.

Usually however a developer will decide to take out a mortgage. When the loan is being negotiated there are a number of factors which need to be considered to ensure the best possible terms. The first is the interest rate. The rates offered by the various mortgage lending institutions should be checked to see which are the most competitive. The Dominion Interest Act requires that the mortgage agreement shall state the amount of principal and the rate of interest to be compounded yearly or half yearly, not in advance. The effect of this is that although mortgage repayments may be made monthly, the interest cannot be compounded more frequently than semi-annually. This will be dealt with in more detail in the next chapter, but compounding semi-annually means that interest is calculated every six months at half the stated annual rate of interest.

Some mortgage lenders will discount the loan in order to obtain a better yield. When doing this they charge interest on the principal amount stated in the mortgage agreement, but the actual amount of money advanced to the borrower is less. The effect is that the mortgagor (the borrower) is receiving less money and effectively paying a higher rate of interest than agreed, and the mortgagee (the lender) is achieving a better rate of return.

Every mortgage has an amortization period and a term, but the two are not necessarily the same. To amortize a loan is to reduce it to zero over a period of time by repaying it in instalments. It comes from the French *a mort* meaning "at the point of death" so the loan is in effect being "killed off". The amortization period is the time required to accomplish this and it, together with the interest rate and the size of the loan will govern the amount of the repayments. It is usual for repayments to be made in equal monthly instalments, although other arrangements can be made, with part of the payment going toward interest and the balance going toward repayment of the principal. While the amortization period can be twenty-five years or more the term is usually considerably less, probably no more than five years. The term is the period of time at the end of which the mortgagee can ask for its money back. If the mortgagor cannot repay the loan at the end of the term it has to renew the mortgage or arrange financing elsewhere to pay off the mortgagee, but in any case it may have to pay a different, and possibly higher, rate of interest than it was paying on the original mortgage and its monthly payments will change.

At one time it was not uncommon for the amortization period and the term to be the same, but as interest rates climbed and mortgagees found themselves with long-term loans at low rates of interest, they reduced the length of the term in order to take advantage of the higher rates which became available. With commercial developments a longer term might be arranged and it is up to the developer to find a mortgage lender which will provide the money with a term which suits the development.

Another factor which the developer has to consider is the prepayment privileges which will be included in the mortgage agreement. If the mortgage is an open mortgage the mortgagor can discharge the mortgage at any time by paying off the loan without incurring a penalty. Direct N.H.A. loans made with Canada Mortgage and Housing Corporation are usually of this type. With most other lending institutions there will be some form of penalty if the mortgagor wishes to pay off the mortgage before the end of the term, the amount and type of penalty depending on the requirements of the Dominion Interest Act, the age of the mortgage, the current interest rates and the current demand for mortgage loans.

A fairly recent innovation on commercial properties is for the mortgagee to require participation in the development by claiming additional payments if the income is greater than was anticipated. Any developer entering into this form of agreement should make sure that something is obtained in return for losing the additional income if the development proves to be successful.

In some provinces the mortgagee is permitted to restrict the loan to the original mortgagor only. In this case, since the mortgage cannot be transferred, any purchaser of the developer's property would have to arrange its own financing, or the developer would have to lend the money to the purchaser in the form of a second mortgage to enable the sale to go through. This could result in complications if the purchaser subsequently wished to sell the property again.

A mortgage is a charge against real estate, with a first mortgage taking precedence over second and subsequent mortgages. Mortgage institutions will normally lend only up to a certain percentage of the appraised value of a development. This means that the balance will have to be found by the developer and, if it doesn't have the money or doesn't wish to invest it in the development, it will have to borrow it elsewhere as a second mortgage. A second mortgage can only become a first mortgage when the original first mortgage has been discharged, at which time any subsequent mortgages would also move up a step in precedence. If the mortgagor defaults in repayments on the first mortgage the mortgagee can, after taking the necessary legal steps, foreclose on the property, wipe out all subsequent charges and become the owner of the property with a clear title. This is one of the reasons why second and subsequent mortgages have higher interest rates – the risk is greater because the mortgagor may default on the first mortgage and these mortgagees would then lose their money. A second or subsequent mortgagee can also take action for foreclosure if the mortgagor fails to make payment. However, in this case the mortgagee would become liable for repayment of the loans to all mortgagees which have a higher ranking , while those with a lower ranking would find themselves in the same position as in the previous case, they would lose their money.

The best time to apply for long-term financing is when the building is completed and leasing is well under way. Few lending institutions are keen to offer money when all they can see is a building site and a set of drawings. The following is the basic information which is needed when applying for a mortgage:

1. A pro-forma showing the financial feasibility of the development.
2. A copy of the working drawings and specifications of the building if the application is being made before construction starts. These would be reviewed by the lending institution's staff and by outside consultants to determine whether the development is viable.
3. A list of proposed tenancies together with the lease agreements showing the rental terms if they are available. If the mortgage has been arranged prior to the completion of construction it is not unusual for

the lender to require a certain percentage of the building to be leased before it will finalize the agreement.

4. Financial statements of the development company or, if it is a company formed specifically for the development, of the parent company, accompanied by details of the people who are putting the project together. The last thing the lending institution wants is to become the owner of the building and it therefore likes to check not only the ability of the borrower to keep up the mortgage payments but also a willingness to do so.

Provided the developer meets the lending institutions's criteria for the loan it will be given a commitment, which is a preliminary contract to provide the loan, and may be asked for a holding deposit of about one or two per cent of the loan, which may or may not be refunded when the mortgage agreement is signed. A non-refundable holding deposit is another way the mortgagee can increase its earnings.

To illustrate how financing can affect the profitability of a development, consider an industrial building of 930 m² which can be rented at $12.90 per m² and which costs $100,000 to build. Three means of financing are available: by the developer providing all cash (Method A); by means of a mortgage of $75,000 at 9.75% interest with an amortization period of fifteen years (Method B); and by means of a mortgage of $60,000 at 10.25% interest with an amortization period of twenty-five years (Method C). At first sight it would appear that of the three, Method A is probably the best since none of the income has to be paid out in mortgage repayments, while Method B is undoubtedly better than Method C because it has a lower rate of interest and is paid off quicker. A tabulation of the figures shows the following:

	Method A	**Method B**	**Method C**
Capital cost	$100,000	$100,000	$100,000
Mortgage	-	75,000	60,000
Developer's equity	$100,000	$25,000	$40,000
Net income:			
930 m² @ $12.90	12,000	12,000	12,000
Annual mortgage payments:			
Method A	-		
Method B $75,000 x 12.58		9,435	
Method C $60,000 x 10.94			6,564
Net Income	$12,000	$2,565	$5,436

Return on equity:

Method A: $\dfrac{12,000}{100,000}$ 12%

Method B: $\dfrac{2,565}{25,000}$ 10.26%

Method C: $\dfrac{5,436}{40,000}$ 13.59%

Method C therefore gives the best rate of return, followed by Method A and then Method B, although a change in the income or the total cost may give quite different results. The developer's equity is different for each method because in two cases the mortgage lender is providing some of the capital, thus reducing the amount the developer has to contribute. The multipliers of 12.58 and 10.94 given for calculating the annual mortgage payments are obtained from mortgage amortization tables and show the annual amount to be paid for principal and interest in order to pay off $100 at the given rate of interest for the given amortization period.

This example shows how leverage can work. By borrowing $60,000 at 10.25% interest for a period of twenty-five years the developer can obtain a better return on its investment than it can if it uses its own money. A quick way of telling whether leverage will work in any given circumstance is to compare the rate of return using all cash, sometimes known as the natural constant, with the multiplier for annual mortgage payments for the particular interest rate and length of the loan found in the mortgage tables. In the example, the multiplier for Method B is 12.58 which is higher than the natural constant of 12.00 (the return on equity for Method A), an indication that this method of financing is taking more than its share of the net income and will not therefore provide any leverage. On the other hand the multiplier for Method C is 10.94, lower than the natural constant, showing that this method will provide leverage. This comparison with the natural constant does not necessarily rank alternative methods of borrowing in order of merit, it just compares a method of borrowing with not borrowing at all to see whether leverage can be obtained.

One further point in connection with leverage is that it can work in reverse, so the developer has to be very sure of the figures. If the developer found that instead of obtaining $12.90 per m² in rent it could only obtain $10.50 per m², or if the capital cost were to increase, the return on equity for both Methods B and C would drop below the return for Method A. Even worse, if it found it couldn't rent the building at all it would still have to make its mortgage payments, without having any income to cover them.

The method of calculating the return on equity in this example, while it serves its purpose for the example, does not give a true rate of return, as will be explained in Chapter 10.

CHAPTER 9

Time and Money

Money has a different value depending on when it is received and for how long it is kept. This is due to two factors: inflation, which tends to reduce its value; and interest, which increases its value over a period of time. This chapter will deal with the second factor, the effects of investing money and earning interest.

Most people have to spend much of their income when they receive it, but if they have any left over they will want to save it. One way of saving money is to keep it under the mattress, but this is not to be recommended because money under the mattress doesn't earn interest, and inflation will cause it to lose value over time. A better way of saving is to invest it since, whether money is spent or saved, everyone likes to receive something worthwhile in return.

SIMPLE INTEREST

Money is invested with the intention that it should earn interest. Interest is a charge for the use of the money, and the interest earned will depend upon the amount of money invested, the length of time it is invested, and the rate of interest expressed as an annual percentage. It will also depend upon whether the interest is to be calculated as simple or compound interest.

With simple interest only the principal, that is the original amount of the investment, will earn interest. If a thousand dollars is invested at ten per cent per annum simple interest for five years, the interest at the end of the first year would be one hundred dollars. Because only the principal earns interest, it would also be a hundred dollars at the end of each of the remaining four years, for a total of five hundred dollars. The formula for calculating simple interest is:

$$I = Pin$$

where $I =$ the total amount of interest

$P =$ the principal amount

$i =$ the rate of interest (10% = 0.10, 6% = 0.06 etc.)

and $n =$ the time period of the investment.

Thus the interest earned on $1,000 at 10% per annum for five years at simple interest is:

$1,000 x 0.10 x 5 = $500

COMPOUND INTEREST

Simple interest earns the same interest each year over a given period of time. Many GICs are offered at simple interest and this is acceptable if it is intended to spend the interest each year, or if it is intended to reinvest it at a different rate. However, if the interest is to be reinvested each year at the same rate over a given period of time it is better to use compound interest. When money is deposited at compound interest the interest is automatically added to the principal each year, and the two combined will earn further interest at the same rate.

If a thousand dollars is invested at ten per cent compound interest for five years it will be worth $1,100 at the end of the first year. This will become the new principal amount and will earn interest of $110 by the end of the second year to give a total of $1,210. This will continue until at the end of the fifth year the total amount of interest will be $610.51 and the original investment of a thousand dollars will have accumulated

77

to $1,610.51. This is known as the terminal value of the investment, its amount depending on the amount of the investment, the rate of interest and the length of time of the investment. The terminal value also depends upon the investment being made immediately. It will not be the same if the investment is delayed for six months since then there will be a period of six months when the money is not earning interest.

Besides finding the terminal value of an investment there are other calculations needed by an investor to find out the effect of time on money and because they can become quite complicated, discount tables, or interest and annuity tables for real estate appraisers, have been published. The tables give the amounts for the various functions based on a value of one at differing rates of interest and over different time periods. This eliminates the need to calculate the figures each time they are needed, apart from multiplying the figure obtained from the tables by the actual sums being used. Most computer spreadsheet programs have built-in functions which can also do the calculations, as can electronic calculators with built-in financial functions or with an exponential function. In fact an electronic calculator with these functions can, with practice, be quicker than looking up the figures in the tables, and it has the added advantage that it is not limited to those interest rates which are published in the tables.

Future Worth of One (A)

THE FUTURE WORTH OF ONE, also known as THE AMOUNT OF ONE, is the terminal value of one (dollar, pound, mark etc.) invested now at a given rate of compound interest over a given period of time, and is the basis for all other calculations. It is shown graphically in Figure 9 (a).

If an amount of one is to be invested at compound interest at a rate i per annum, it will have amounted to $1+i$ at the end of the first year. By the end of the second year, the interest earned during that year will be $(1+i)i$, and this together with the amount invested at the beginning of the second year (that is the original principal plus the interest earned during the first year) will give a terminal value of:

$$(1 + i) + (1 + i) i$$
$$= (1 + i) + (i + i^2)$$
$$= 1 + 2i + i^2$$
$$= (1 + i)^2$$

Interest earned during the third year will be $(1 + 2i + i^2) i$, so the terminal value at the end of the third year will be:

$$(1 + 2i + i^2) + (1 + 2i + i^2) i$$
$$= (1 + 2i + i^2) + (i + 2i^2 + i^3)$$
$$= 1 + 3i + 3i^2 + i^3$$
$$= (1 + i)^3$$

By extension it can be seen that the formula for calculating the Future Worth of One is:

$$A = (1 + i)^n$$

where $A =$ the future worth of one (sometimes written as S^n)

        $i =$ the rate of interest

and $n =$ the time period of the investment.

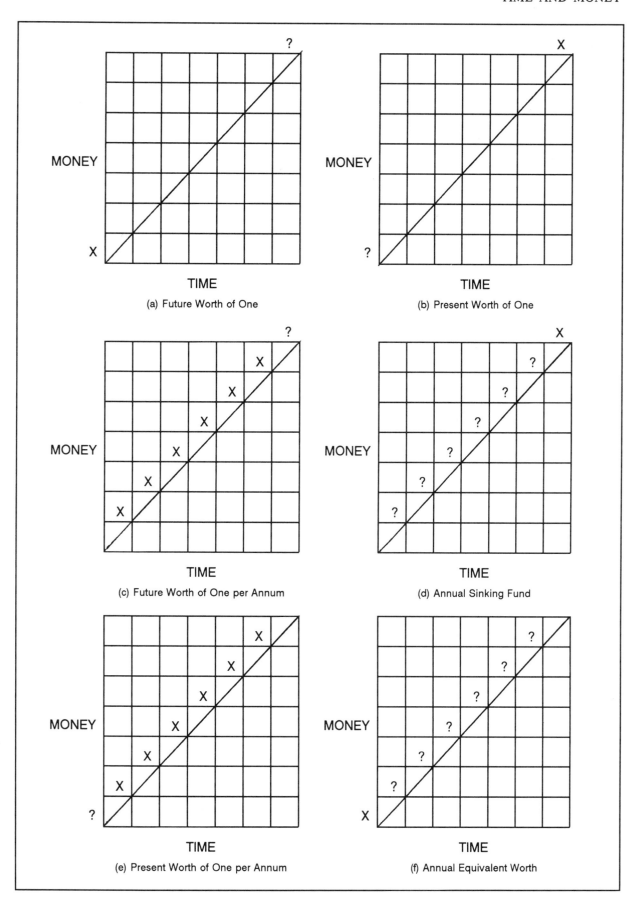

Figure 9

CONSTRUCTION BUDGETING

This formula, when multiplied by the principal, will give its future value. Note that the rate of interest and the time period should correspond. If the rate of interest is an annual rate then the time period should be in years, and if the time period is in months then the rate of interest should be a monthly rate. This will be raised again when compounding periods are considered.

Example: How much will $150 amount to in 21 years if it is invested at 6% per annum compound interest?

Answer:
$150 x $(1 + 0.06)^{21}$
= $150 x 3.3996
= $509.94

Present Worth of One (V)

THE PRESENT WORTH OF ONE is the amount which must be invested now at a given rate of compound interest to accumulate to one over a given period of time, and is shown graphically in Figure 9 (b).

This is the reverse of the Future Worth of One. Whereas the Future Worth of One tells the investor how much one will amount to in the future if it is invested now at compound interest, the Present Worth of One tells the investor how much must be invested now for it to accumulate to one over a given period of time at compound interest.

A little thought will show that the Present Worth of One is the reciprocal of the Future Worth of One, so the formula is:

$$V = \frac{1}{(1 + i)^n} \quad \text{or} \quad V = \frac{1}{A}$$

where $V =$ the present worth of one (sometimes written as V^n)

The present worth is sometimes also referred to as the present value or deferred value and calculating the present worth of a sum which will not be received until some time in the future is known as deferring or discounting that sum.

Example: How much should be invested now to produce $1,000 in 12 years if it is invested at 6% per annum compound interest?

Answer:
$$\$1,000 \times \frac{1}{(1 + 0.065)^{12}}$$

= $1,000 × 0.4697

= $469.70

Future Worth of One per Annum (FV)

THE FUTURE WORTH OF ONE PER ANNUM, also known as the AMOUNT OF ONE PER ANNUM is the terminal value of one (dollar, pound etc.) invested each year at a given rate of compound interest over a given period of time, and is shown graphically in Figure 9 (c).

An annuity is a series of equal payments made at regular intervals, and the future value of an annuity can be calculated using the formula for the Future Worth of One Per Annum, although with many annuities the payments are not made annually but monthly or quarterly, in which case the interest rate and time periods must be adjusted accordingly as will be described later.

The formula for calculating the Future Worth of One Per Annum will vary depending on whether the money is invested, or payments start, at the beginning or the end of each period. When payments are made at the end of the period, as for example mortgage repayments which start a month after the loan is made, it is known as an ordinary annuity. The formula for calculating the Future Worth of One Per Annum when the payments are made at the *end* of the period is:

$$FV = \frac{(1 + i)^n - 1}{i} \quad \text{or} \quad \frac{A - 1}{i}$$

where $FV =$ the future worth of one per period.

When payments are made at the beginning of the period, as for example insurance premiums or bank deposits which are made immediately, it is known as an annuity due. The formula for calculating the Future Worth of One Per Annum when the investment is made at the *beginning* of the period is:

$$FV = \frac{(1 + i)^{n + 1} - 1}{i} - 1$$

Example: How much will $150 a year amount to in 21 years if invested at 6% per annum compound interest (a) with the first instalment being made immediately, and (b) with the first instalment being made in a year's time?

Answer: (a)

$$\$150 \times \frac{1.06^{22} - 1}{0.06} - 1$$

$$= \$150 \times 42.3923$$

$$= \$6,358.85$$

(b)

$$\$150 \times \frac{1.06^{21} - 1}{0.06}$$

$$= \$150 \times 39.9927$$

$$= \$5,998.91$$

Note that the time period for (a) is a year longer than for (b) because the first deposit will start earning interest immediately.

Annual Sinking Fund (SF)

THE ANNUAL SINKING FUND factor is the amount which must be invested each year to accumulate to one at a given rate of compound interest over a given period of time. It is shown graphically in Figure 9 (c).

When a corporation or government issues bonds it knows that, besides paying interest on the bonds, it will have to repay the loan when the bonds mature. In order to ensure that it can meet the repayment at maturity it creates (or should create) a separate fund into which it makes equal periodic deposits which, with compound interest, will equal the amount of the loan by the time the loan has to be repaid. This is called a sinking fund because its purpose is to sink, or shrink, the debt. The interest on the sinking fund is not necessarily at the same rate as the interest paid on the bonds.

The same applies to developers who are putting up new buildings. A building, unlike land, is a wasting asset because eventually it will come to the end of its life and have to be replaced. If the developers don't put aside part of their income and deposit it in a sinking fund they will be left one day with a piece of land with no building on it, and insufficient capital to construct a new one. Whether, in fact, they do so is a decision they have to make and they may decide not to, but nevertheless a sinking fund is usually incorporated in the calculation of the present value of a development.

Sinking fund payments are made at the end of each period so the formula is the reciprocal of the Future Worth of One Per Annum when the investment is made at the end of the period, thus:

$$SF = \frac{i}{(1 + i)^n - 1} \quad \text{or} \quad \frac{i}{A - 1}$$

where $SF =$ the sinking fund factor.

Example: How much should be invested at the end of each year to produce $5,000 in 10 years' time at 6% per annum compound interest?

Answer:
$$\$5,000 \times \frac{0.06}{1.06^{10} - 1}$$

$$= \$5,000 \times 0.07587$$

$$= \$379.35$$

Present Worth of One per Annum (YP)

THE PRESENT WORTH OF ONE PER ANNUM, which is shown graphically in Figure 9 (e), will depend upon whether the income is to be earned in perpetuity, or whether there is a limited life to it and, if it has a limited life, whether the income starts immediately or starts at the end of the first period.

If an investment of $100,000 is made in say, a piece of land and the investor expects to receive a 10% return on the investment, the annual income to be expected will be:

$$\frac{10}{100} \times \$100,000 = \$10,000$$

This return is based on simple interest because the land is not a wasting asset, unlike a building which will eventually wear out and have to be replaced. The income is therefore perpetual and there is no need to make provision for replacing the capital.

Reversing the process, if the investor wishes to invest a sum of money which will give a 10% return amounting to $10,000 a year, the amount needed to be invested is:

$$\frac{100}{10} \times \$10,000 = \$100,000$$

The multiplier which has to be applied to the annual income to give the capital investment is known as the PRESENT WORTH OF ONE PER ANNUM IN PERPETUITY. In the United Kingdom it is also known as YEARS' PURCHASE. It can be calculated very easily by dividing one hundred by the rate of interest, thus:

If the rate of interest is 5%, $\quad YP = \dfrac{100}{5}$ or 20

If the rate of interest is 4%, $\quad YP = \dfrac{100}{4}$ or 25

If the rate of interest is 6%, $\quad YP = \dfrac{100}{6}$ or 16.67

These calculations apply only when the income is perpetual.

An investor who purchases an income for a limited time is in quite a different position from the purchaser of a perpetual income. Whereas the purchaser of a perpetual income can expect to receive the income for life, or until the investment is sold, the purchaser of an income for a limited time will receive the income only for that period and will then lose not only the income but also the initial investment. This means that the purchaser of an income-producing property will need to make two calculations to find its present value, one for the land using simple interest and another for the building. The one for the building will need to incorporate a sinking fund so that it can be replaced at the end of its life and the formula to be used is the PRESENT WORTH OF ONE PER ANNUM, also known as the INWOOD ANNUITY FACTOR or YEARS' PURCHASE WITH A LIMITED TERM. This formula gives the amount which must be invested now to give an income of one per year, together with a sinking fund to replace the original capital, at given rates of simple interest for the investment and compound interest for the sinking fund, over a given period of time.

In most circumstances the income starts at the end of the first period, not immediately, and it has to equal the amount of interest plus the sinking fund, that is i + SF. Since the capital investment (P) equals the income times the Years' Purchase, then:

$$P = (i + SF) \times YP$$

$$\text{and } YP = \frac{P}{(i + SF)}$$

where $YP =$ the present worth of one per period.

In finding the Present Worth of One Per Annum where the capital investment is one, the formula becomes:

$$YP = \frac{1}{i + SF} \qquad \text{or} \qquad \frac{1}{i + \dfrac{i}{(1 + i)^n - 1}}$$

This is the most common formula for calculating the Present Worth of One Per Annum.

CONSTRUCTION BUDGETING

It is not usual to start receiving an income immediately on an investment, but in the event that this does occur the formula becomes:

$$YP = \left(\frac{1}{i + SF}\right)(1 + i) \qquad \text{or} \qquad \left(\frac{1}{i + \dfrac{i}{(1 + i)^n - 1}}\right)(1 + i)$$

Note that in these formulae there are in fact two rates of interest involved, one known as the remunerative rate which is used to provide the income, and a second known as the accumulative rate which is used to provide the sinking fund when the investment ceases. For this reason some of the published discount tables give two separate tables for the Present Worth of One Per Annum, a single rate table and a dual rate table. A single rate table gives figures when the remunerative interest rate and the accumulative interest rate are assumed to be the same, while the dual rate table gives the figures when the two rates are different. In the past the accumulative rate for the sinking fund was lower than the remunerative rate because it was assumed that the sinking fund investment would be in low-risk bonds, or in a sinking fund policy taken out with an insurance company, either of which would bear low interest rates. It is usual these days, however, to assume that both rates will be the same, and when referring to published tables it is the single rate table which is normally used.

Example: How much should be invested in a building which will be demolished in ten years' time if an income of $20,000 a year can be expected from it, and the rate is assumed to be 6%?

Answer:
$$\$20,000 \times \frac{1}{0.06 + \dfrac{0.06}{1.06^{10} - 1}}$$

$$= \$20,000 \times 7.3601$$

$$= \$147,202$$

Annual Equivalent Worth (AEW)

The ANNUAL EQUIVALENT WORTH, also known as the PARTIAL PAYMENT FACTOR, gives the annual income which will be earned on an investment of one at a given rate of interest over a given period of time, and is shown graphically in Figure 9 (f).

Because it is the reciprocal of the Present Worth of One Per Annum it will have the same variations. If the income is to be received in perpetuity the income will be the amount of the investment times the interest rate. If, however, it is to be received for a limited time so that the sinking fund has to be taken into consideration and income is to start at the end of the first period, the formula for the Annual Equivalent Worth, based on an investment of one, will be:

$$AEW = i + SF \qquad \text{or} \qquad i + \frac{i}{(1 + i)^n - 1}$$

where $AEW =$ the annual equivalent worth of one.

This formula can also be used for calculating the payments required to amortize a mortgage.

Example: If $150 is invested at 6% for 21 years, what will the annual income be, assuming that the principal will be lost at the end of the investment?

Answer: $$\$150 \times 0.06 + \frac{0.06}{1.06^{21} - 1}$$

$$= \$150 \times 0.085$$

$$= \$12.75$$

If the income is to be received immediately rather than starting at the end of the first period, the formula will be:

$$AEW = (i + SF) \qquad \text{or} \qquad \left(i + \frac{i}{(1 + i)^n - 1} \right) (1 + i)$$

COMPOUNDING PERIODS

All the examples given so far in this chapter have assumed that compounding will take place annually, although reference was made earlier to the fact that it might take place more frequently. When compounding takes place annually the assumption is that the principal will remain invested for a year, the interest will then be added to it, the two together will accrue interest at the end of the second year, and so on year by year with interest being added on as an annual event. With annual compounding therefore, i in the formulae will always be the annual interest rate, and n will always be the number of years over which the investment will take place.

Interest is not always compounded annually. It can be compounded semi-annually, quarterly, monthly, weekly or even more frequently. If, for example, interest is to be compounded quarterly, interest is calculated at the end of the first quarter, added to the principal, and the two combined are carried forward for interest to be calculated at the end of the second quarter, and so on, for the life of the investment. In other words interest is added, not as an annual event but as a quarterly event. This does not affect the formulae but means that i is no longer an annual rate and n is no longer in years. To illustrate what happens when compounding is done more frequently than annually, suppose one hundred dollars is to be invested at eight per cent for one year. The future value at various compounding periods will be as follows:

Annual:	$100 x (1 + 0.08)^1$	=	$108.00
Semi-annually:	$100 x (1 + 0.04)^2$	=	$108.16
Quarterly:	$100 x (1 + 0.02)^4$	=	$108.24
Monthly:	$100 x (1 + 0.00667)^{12}$	=	$108.30

When compounding more frequently than annually n becomes the number of compounding periods rather than the number of years, and i is the annual interest rate divided by the number of compounding periods in a year. This example also shows that by compounding more frequently than annually an investor will receive a better rate of return on the money. In fact, although the nominal or stated rate is eight per cent in each calculation, by compounding monthly the actual or effective rate has been increased to 8.30%. When compounding annually the nominal and the effective rate will be the same, but when compounding more frequently the effective rate will always be higher than the nominal rate.

Compounding more frequently than annually is of particular interest when calculating mortgage repayments.

Example: What will the monthly payments be on a mortgage of $30,000 with an amortization period of 25 years at an annual interest rate of 11%, compounded monthly?

Answer:

$$AEW = i + \frac{i}{(1 + i)^n - 1}$$

$$= 0.00917 + \frac{0.00917}{1.00917^{300} - 1}$$

$$= 0.00980$$

Monthly payments $= \$30,000 \times 0.00980$

$$= \$294.00$$

Note that the interest rate is shown as a monthly rate (0.11 divided by $12 = 0.00917$) and n is the number of months (25 times $12 = 300$).

In Canada, as was mentioned in the last chapter, the Dominion Interest Act stipulates that interest on a mortgage cannot be compounded more frequently than semi-annually, although payments may be made monthly. This means that although the principal is being reduced each month as part of the mortgage payment, the compounding can take place only every six months, which introduces an added complication. It is solved by adjusting the nominal interest rate to an effective monthly rate by means of a further formula which is:

$$\text{Effective monthly rate} = \left(1 + \frac{i}{2}\right)^{\frac{1}{6}} - 1$$

Example: What will be the monthly payments in the previous example if interest is to be compounded semi-annually?

Answer:

$$\text{Effective monthly rate} = \left(1 + \frac{0.11}{2}\right)^{\frac{1}{6}} - 1$$

$$= 0.00896$$

$$AEW = i + \frac{i}{(1 + i)^n - 1}$$

$$= 0.00896 + \frac{0.00896}{1.00896^{300} - 1}$$

$$= 0.00963$$

Monthly payments $= \$30,000 \times 0.00963$

$$= \$288.90$$

These calculations are onerous if they have to be done by hand, but fortunately tables are readily available for Canadian amortization schedules. An electronic calculator with exponential or financial functions makes the calculations comparatively easy if tables are not available.

CHAPTER 10

Yield Analysis

YIELD

Yield is the return an investor expects to make on an investment, usually expressed as a percentage. For many investments the calculation of the yield is fairly simple; a mortgagee for instance knows that, subject to the mortgagor defaulting, the yield will be the stipulated interest rate on the unpaid balance of the mortgage. Similarly, a bond purchased at face value will give a yield which is the same as the nominal rate of the bond. However, if the bond is bought at anything other than the face value, the yield will be different from the nominal rate. As an example, a bond with a face value of $1,000 and selling at face value will yield $50 a year if its nominal rate is 5%, so the yield and the nominal rate are the same. If the bond can be bought for $850 the income will still be $50 a year but the yield will be:

$$\frac{50}{850} \times 100 = 5.88\%$$

This simple example shows that a comparison of incomes receivable from investments should be made on the yields, not on the nominal interest rates. It also shows that a fall in the price of a security will result in a rise in the yield, while a rise in price will reduce the yield, assuming the yield is based solely on the income from the interest.

For the real estate investor the calculation of the yield becomes more complicated, since it has to be made on a number of assumptions. In some instances the yield will be based solely on the income to be derived from the property, in which case assumptions have to be made about the income – whether it will remain constant throughout the life of the investment, whether it is likely to increase over the years, or whether it might decline. In other instances the investor may assume the property will be sold after a few years, in which case additional assumptions have to be made about the selling price – whether it will be the same as the cost, whether it will be more than the cost, or whether it will result in a capital loss.

All investors will have their own objectives and priorities when making investment decisions. Generally they will be to maximize cash flow and improve capital gain prospects, but they might also include considerations of prestige, amenities and tax implications. To the extent that an investor may be prepared to accept higher or lower yields, the criteria by which investments are usually judged are as follows:

1. SECURITY OF INCOME

The investor likes to be assured that there will be a regular income from the investment and, even more importantly, that the income will keep pace with inflation. An adequate income now could prove to be inadequate in the future if the purchasing power of money declines rapidly. An investor who can be assured that the income is secure and will increase at the same, or at a better, rate than the decline in the value of money is likely to be prepared to accept a lower yield than if there is no such assurance.

2. SECURITY OF CAPITAL

As with security of income, the investor likes to be assured that the value of the investment will keep pace with inflation. If an investor buys a piece of property which has appreciated in value by fifty per cent when it is sold five years later it might be said that there has been a gain of fifty per cent. But if all other commodities have also appreciated by fifty per cent, then in real terms there has been no gain at all, and the value of the asset is relatively the same as when it was bought. When there is no tax on capital gains, many investors are concerned less about the annual income from the investment and are prepared to accept a lower yield if it can be shown that there is likely to be an appreciation of capital over the years.

3. LIQUIDITY

This refers to the ease with which an asset can be converted into cash and can also encompass the acceptability of the asset as collateral for a loan. Real estate is not as liquid as say, stocks traded on the stock market, and an investor would require a higher yield on a real estate investment than on an investment in stocks and bonds.

4. TRANSFER COSTS

The acceptable yield would depend to some extent on the costs to invest the capital and to subsequently convert it back into cash. Stocks incur brokerage fees when they are sold but are relatively inexpensive to sell compared with real estate which involves brokerage, appraisal and legal fees.

5. MANAGEMENT

Real estate investments require management of the investment portfolio, more so than investments in government bonds, and the investor would therefore expect a higher yield. In this context management does not refer to the day-to-day management of the property but to decisions about the buying and selling of real estate.

6. LEGISLATION

Most types of investment are affected to some degree by government legislation, but none to the same extent as real estate. An investor whose investment may be affected by rent controls or some other form of legislation restricting the income will require a higher yield.

CAPITALIZATION

In Chapter 7 it was stated that a feasibility study attempts to show that the value of a real estate development at least equals its cost. The capital cost of a development is comparatively easy to determine, but its value, since it refers to present value, is less easy to find because it requires assumptions to be made about future incomes and expenses which then have to be discounted, using the formulae described in the last chapter. Discounting needs interest rates, known as capitalization rates, and the investor needs to find the capitalization rate which is also the yield rate.

Table 7 shows the figures for a simple development in which the developer will be providing all the capital.

Example 1:   What is the capitalization rate for the development shown in Table 7?

Capital Costs:	Land	$100,000
	Building and development costs	900,000
	Total capital costs (Owner's equity)	$1,000,000
Gross Annual Income:		$170,000
Gross Annual Expenses:		
	Operating and maintenance costs	$70,000
Net Annual Income:		$100,000

Table 7

Capital Costs:	Land	$100,000
	Building and development costs	900,000
	Total	$1,000,000
Gross Annual Income:		$170,000
Gross Annual Expenses:		
	Operating and maintenance costs	70,000
	Mortgage repayments	86,628
	Total	$156,628
Net Annual Income:		$13,372
Owner's equity:	Total capital costs	$1,000,000
	Less Mortgage	750,000
	Total	$250,000

Table 8

Answer: The capitalization rate will be the net annual income divided by the owner's equity which in this instance is the total cost, multiplied by one hundred:

$$\frac{\$100,000}{\$1,000,000} \times 100 = 10\%$$

This example assumes that the developer's own capital will be used to finance the project, which is unusual. Table 8 shows the same development, but this time the developer has taken a mortgage of $750,000 with interest at 11% and an amortization period of twenty-five years.

Example 2: What is the capitalization rate for the development shown in table 8?

Answer: The capitalization rate will be the net annual income divided by the owner's equity, multiplied by one hundred:

$$\frac{\$13,372}{250,000} \times 100 = 5.35\%$$

NET PRESENT VALUE

In Example 1 the capitalization rate is shown to be 10%, and in Example 2 it is shown to be 5.35%, but are they also the yield? Will the developer receive these returns on the investments? The answer to these questions is found by capitalizing the future incomes from the property to find their present value, and if the present value is equal to the investment, then the capitalization rate is also the yield. This requires the use of the formulae described in the last chapter, the Present Worth of One Dollar Per Annum (YP) for future annual income, and the Present Worth of One Dollar (V) for future lump sum incomes. In the next example a capitalization rate of ten per cent will be used since this is the rate found in Example 1.

Example 3: If the developer expects to sell the development shown in Table 7 after ten years for $1,000,000 will the yield be 10%?

Answer: Income $100,000 x YP, 10 years @ 10%
= $100,000 x 6.144567   = $614,457

Sale $1,000,000 x V, 10 years @ 10%
= $1,000,000 x 0.385543   =   385,543

Total Present Value $1,000,000

The total present value equals the owner's equity, so the yield will be 10%.

Example 4: If the developer expects to sell the same development after twenty years for $1,000,000 will the yield still be 10%?

Answer:	Income	$100,000 x YP, 20 years @ 10%		
		= $100,000 x 8.51356	=	$851,356
	Sale	$1,000,000 x V, 20 years @ 10%		
		= $1,000,000 x 0.148644	=	148,644
	Total Present Value			$1,000,000

The total present value still equals the owner's equity, so the yield will still be 10%.

Example 5: If the developer expects to sell the same development after ten years for $1,500,000 will the yield still be 10%?

Answer:	Income	$100,000 x YP, 10 years @ 10%		
		= $100,000 x 6.144567	=	$614,457
	Sale	$1,500,000 x V, 10 years @ 10%		
		= $1,500,000 x 0.385543	=	578,315
	Total Present Value			$1,192,772

The total present value is now more than the owner's equity so the yield will be more than 10%. This is because of the capital gain made on the sale.

In the next example the land, being a non-wasting asset, has been separated from the building and development costs when calculating the present value.

Example 6: If the developer decides to hold the property for 40 years, at which time it is expected to be demolished, will the yield still be 10%?

Answer:	Net annual income		$100,000
	Return required on land:		
	$100,000 x AEW in perpetuity @ 10%		
	= $100,000 x 0.10	=	10,000
	Balance attributable to the building		$90,000
	Income $90,000 x YP, 40 years @ 10%		
	= $90,000 x 9.779051	=	880,115
	Present value of the land		100,000
	Total Present Value		$980,115

The total present value is now less than the owner's equity so the yield will be less than 10%.

91

CONSTRUCTION BUDGETING

An alternative method similar to that used in the previous examples will give the same answer:

Income	$100,000 x YP, 40 years @ 10%		
	= $100,000 x 9.779051	=	$977,905
Residual land value $100,000 x V, 40 years @ 10%			
	= $100,000 x 0.022095	=	2,210
Total Present Value			$980,115

Only if the land were to increase in value so that it becomes worth the amount of the initial investment of one million dollars in forty years time (which is not impossible) would the present value equal the owner's equity.

When the developer takes out a mortgage to help finance the project, similar calculations can be made.

Example 7:   If the developer expects to sell the development shown in Table 8 after ten years for $1,000,000, will the yield be 5.35%?

Answer:	Income	$13,372 x YP, 10 years @ 5.35%	
		= $13,372 x 7.592155	=	$101,522
	Sale	$1,000,000 x V, 10 years @ 5.35%	
		= $1,000,000 x 0.593820	=	593,820
	Total Present Value		$695,342

The present value is more than the developer's equity of $250,000 so the yield is more than 5.35%.

This example shows how leverage has improved the developer's position. Only if the property were sold for $250,000, the amount of the original equity, would the yield have been 5.35%. As it is, every time a mortgage payment is made a portion of the principal is paid back, thus building up the developer's equity in the development and increasing the yield.

These examples show that, while the calculation of the capitalization rate shown Examples 1 and 2 may give an indication of the viability of a project, it is most unlikely that it will give the yield that can be expected. Examples 3 and 4 show that time is not a factor in deriving the present value to check the yield rate. What is important is the income and the residual value of the property at the end of the investment. The capitalization rate will equal the yield only if:

(a) The income remains constant throughout the life of the investment, and
(b) Exactly the amount of the developer's equity can be recovered at the end of the investment.

These two requirements are seldom met, except in the case of an investment such as a mortgage loan where the mortgagee receives interest payments regularly throughout the term of the mortgage and recovers exactly the amount of the principal at the termination of the mortgage. Otherwise it is rare that the yield will equal the capitalization rate.

All these examples have shown how the capitalization rate can be tested to see whether and under what circumstances it bears any relationship to the yield. For many investments, however, it is unnecessary to calculate the capitalization rate because the investors will be comparing the investments with alternatives to see which gives the better yield. If, for example, a developer knows a yield of, say 9%, can be obtained on a government bond it will be necessary to find out whether a better yield can be obtained by investing in property. The developer therefore knows what yield would be acceptable, and needs to know whether the development will provide it.

Example 8: Will the developer obtain a yield of at least 12% for the development shown in Table 7 if it is expected to be sold after ten years for $1,500,000?

Answer: Example 5 showed that the development will yield more than 10% under these conditions and the question now is whether it will yield as much as 12%.

Income	$100,000 x YP, 10 years @ 12%		
	= $100,000 x 5.650223	=	$565,022
Sale	$1,500,000 x V, 10 years @ 12%		
	= $1,500,000 x 0.321973	=	482,960
			————
Total Present Value			$1,047,982
			=======

The developer will obtain a yield of at least 12% because the present value exceeds the equity.

Very often the net annual income will not be a constant amount but will fluctuate year by year. A cash flow schedule will then have to be prepared showing the net annual income year by year, and each year's income must by discounted at the anticipated yield rate to give a total present value. Hence the term discounted cash flow analysis.

Example 9: A developer has a development which has a total capital cost of $900,000. There will be no mortgage and it is expected to be sold for $1,250,000 after ten years. The anticipated net income is as follows:

Year	1	$80,000	Year	6	$98,000
	2	$90,000		7	$100,000
	3	$95,000		8	$100,000
	4	$97,000		9	$95,000
	5	$100,000		10	$95,000

Will the yield be at least 12%?

Answer: The discounted cash flow will be:

Year	Net Cash Flow	x	V @ 12%	=	Present Value
1	80,000	x	0.892857	=	71,429
2	90,000	x	0.797194	=	71,747
3	95,000	x	0.711780	=	67,619
4	97,000	x	0.635518	=	61,645
5	100,000	x	0.567427	=	56,743
6	98,000	x	0.506631	=	49,650
7	100,000	x	0.452350	=	45,235
8	100,000	x	0.403883	=	40,388
9	95,000	x	0.360610	=	34,258
10	95,000	x	0.321973	=	30,587
10 (Sale)	1,250,000	x	0.321973	=	402,467

Total Present Value $931,768

The development will return a yield of at least 12% because the present value of the income ($931,768) exceeds the owner's equity of $900,000.

The developments shown in Examples 8 and 9 will both return a yield of at least twelve per cent, but if the developer has a choice between the two, which is the better investment? There are two ways in which a decision can be made, the first being to calculate a present value ratio for each so that they can be compared. The present value ratio is the total present value divided by the owner's equity. For examples 8 and 9 the present value ratios will be:

Example 8:
$$\frac{1,047,982}{1,000,000} = 1.047982$$

Example 9:
$$\frac{931,768}{900,000} = 1.035298$$

Both investments will yield at least twelve per cent because the present value ratio in both instances exceeds one, but Example 8 has a higher ratio and is therefore the better investment.

The second way of comparing two investments is by marginal analysis. This compares the present value (benefit) with the cost of each investment, and shows the marginal gain of one investment over the other. For Examples 8 and 9 the marginal analysis will be:

	Example 8		Example 9		Margin
Benefit	$1,047,982	-	$931,768	=	$116,214
Cost	$1,000,000	-	$900,000	=	$100,000
Gain	$47,982	-	$31,768		$16,214

This shows that for an additional expenditure of $100,000 Example 8 makes a gain of $47,982 which is $16,214 higher than Example 9, making it the better investment.

Comparing the present value ratios and making a marginal analysis will always give the same ranking order. However, they assume that the yield on the difference in capital costs between the two developments will be the same. The difference in capital cost between Examples 8 and 9 is $100,000, and these calculations make the assumption that it will also be invested to produce a yield of 12%. But if it were possible to invest it elsewhere at a higher rate, then it might be preferable to choose the development shown in Example 9, and invest the $100,000 elsewhere at the higher rate. This is not very likely since the developer would have selected the yield of 12% because this is presumably the highest yield obtainable in alternative investments.

A greater difficulty arises with respect to differences in the length of time over which an investment takes place.

Example 10: Will the developer obtain a yield of at least 12% for the development shown in Table 7 if it is expected to be sold after five years for $1,250,000? What will the present value ratio be?

Answer:

Income	$100,000 x YP, 5 years @ 12%		
	= $100,000 x 3.604776	=	$360,478
Sale	$1,250,000 x V, 5 years @ 12%		
	= $1,250,000 x 0.567427	=	709,284
	Total Present Value		$1,069,762

The developer will obtain a yield of at least 12%.

The present value ratio will be

$$\frac{1,069,762}{1,000,000} = 1.069762$$

This is a better present value ratio than either of the two previous examples, but the yield has been earned over five years whereas the other two were earned over ten years, so can they really be compared? The answer is that they can be compared provided the assumption is made that the developer will reinvest the money received from the sale for a further five years in an investment which also yields twelve per cent. This is known as a reinvestment assumption. If it is reinvested at any other rate the present value ratio of Example 10 cannot be compared with those found for Examples 8 and 9.

Example 11: If the developer expects to be able to obtain a yield of only 10% for five years upon reinvestment at the conclusion of the investment described in Example 10, will a yield of at least 12% still be obtainable over the next ten years, and what will the present value ratio be?

Answer: This problem has to be solved in three stages. First, the present value found in Example 10 has to be projected forward to give its future value in five years' time using a rate of 12%. Then this value has to be projected forward a further five years using the reduced rate of 10%. Finally, the resulting future value is brought to a present value using a rate of 12% as follows:

(1)   Total present value, as shown in Example 10: $1,069,762
        Future value in five years time:
            $1,069,762 x A, 5 years @ 12%
        = $1,069,762 x 1.762342   = $1,885,286
                                                                    _____

At the end of the first five years the investment will have amounted to $1,885,286 and this is the amount to invest for the next five years at the new rate of 10%. An investment of $1,885,286 in five years time, made over five years with a yield of ten per cent will give a future value ten years from now of:

(2) $1,885,286 x A, 5 years @ 10%
        = $1,885,286 x 1.610510   = $3,036,272
                                                                    _____

The present value of a sum of $3,036,272 in ten years from now will be:

(3) $3,036,272 x V, 10 years @ 12%
        = $3,036,272 x 0.321973   = $977,598
                                                                    ===========

The developer will obtain a yield of less than 12%.

The present value ratio will be $\frac{977,598}{1,000,000}$ = 0.977598

If the developer had been able to obtain a yield of 12% on reinvestment the present value would have been $1,069,762, the same as that found in Example 10.

Sometimes the cash flow may contain negative numbers, say in the early years of a development when it is expected to lose money before it starts earning a profit. In this case the present value of the negative incomes are deducted from the present values of the positive incomes when assessing the total present value.

Example 12: A developer has a development which has a total capital cost of $1,000,000, with no mortgage, and which is expected to be sold for $1,600,000 after five years. The anticipated net income is as follows:

Year		
1	$20,000	loss
2	$5,000	loss
3	$75,000	
4	$100,000	
5	$120,000	

Can it provide a yield of 10%?

Answer: The discounted cash flow will be:

Year	Net Cash Flow	x	V @ 10%	=	Present Value
1	(20,000)	x	0.909091	=	(18,182)
2	(5,000)	x	0.826446	=	(4,132)
3	75,000	x	0.751315	=	56,349
4	100,000	x	0.683013	=	68,301
5	120,000	x	0.620921	=	74,511
5 (Sale)	1,600,000	x	0.620921	=	993,474
	Total Present Value				$1,170,321

The total present value exceeds the equity so the developer will receive a yield of at least 10%.

The present value ratio will be $\dfrac{1,170,321}{1,000,000} = 1.170321$

When a mortgage is used to help finance the project the calculations are complicated by having to work out the balance remaining on the mortgage, if any, but otherwise they are similar to those already described.

Example 13:   Will the developer obtain a yield of at least 12% for the development shown in Table 8 if it is expected to be sold after ten years for $1,500,000?

Answer: Reference to mortgage amortization tables show that in ten years the developer will have repaid $106,212 of the mortgage principal, leaving a balance of $643,788 still to be repaid. Assuming the mortgage can be paid off at that time, or the new owner will assume it, the income from the sale will be:

Sale price		$1,500,000
Less balance of mortgage to be paid off		643,788
Income to the developer		$856,212

Income	$13,372 x YP, 10 years @ 12%		
	= $13,372 x 5.650223	=	$75,555
Sale	$856,212 x V, 10 years @ 12%		
	= $856,212 x 0.321973	=	275,677
	Total Present Value		$351,232

The total present value is higher than the owner's equity ($250,000) so the development will yield at least 12%.

The present value ratio will be

$$\frac{351,232}{250,000} = 1.404928$$

This is a better ratio than was found for Example 8 which was similar, but had no mortgage to help with the financing, and shows again how leverage helps to improve the yield.

INTERNAL RATE OF RETURN

A capitalization calculation will give the yield under certain conditions, and net present value calculations will show whether a capitalization rate is, or close to, the yield, but neither will show what the actual yield will be. To do this the internal rate of return must be found.

The internal rate of return is that rate of interest which makes the present value of future income equal to the owner's equity, so the calculations are very similar to those used when calculating the net present value. When the internal rate of return has been found it will be the yield.

It cannot be calculated directly, but has to be derived by interpolation between two rates which are believed to straddle the internal rate of return. This means that the present value at two assumed yield rates have to be calculated in the same way as was done in the net present value approach and the internal rate of return found between them.

This can be done by finding the rate which makes the present value of future income equal to the owner's equity. Alternatively it can be done by finding the rate which makes the present value ratio equal to one (which amounts to the same thing) and this method will be used in the following examples.

Example 14: What is the internal rate of return (yield) for the development shown in Table 7 if the developer expects to sell the development after ten years for $1,500,000?

Answer: This is the development which was used in Example 8 to show that the yield would exceed twelve per cent. The two rates which will be tested therefore are 12% which is known to be less than the yield, and 15% which is likely to be more than the yield, and the internal rate of return interpolated between them.

			Present Value @12%	Present Value @15%
Income	$100,000 x YP, 10 years @ 12%			
	= $100,000 x 5.650223	=	$565,022	–
	$100,000 x YP, 10 years @ 15%			
	= $100,000 x 5.018769	=	–	501,877
Sale	$1,500,000 x V, 10 years @ 12%			
	= $1,500,000 x 0.321973	=	482,960	–
	$1,500,000 x V, 10 years @ 15%			
	= $1,500,000 x 0.247185	=	–	370,777
Total Present Value			$1,047,982	$872,654

Present value ratio

$$\frac{1,047,982}{1,000,000} \qquad \frac{872,654}{1,000,000}$$

$$= 1.047982 \qquad = 0.872654$$

Since the internal rate of return is that rate where the present value ratio equals one, it must be between twelve and fifteen per cent. The actual rate is found by the following formula:

$$IRR = L\% + \frac{HR - 1.0}{HR - LR} (H\% - L\%)$$

where HR = the higher ratio

LR = the lower ratio

H% = the higher capitalization rate

and L% = the lower capitalization rate

This becomes:

$$IRR = 12\% + \frac{1.047982 - 1.0}{1.047982 - 0.872654} \times (15 - 12)$$

$$= 12\% + \frac{0.047982}{0.175328} \times 3$$

$$= 12\% + 0.82101$$

$$= 12.82\%$$

The internal rate of return (yield) is, say, 12.8%

The formula used in this example gives a straight-line interpolation which is generally considered to be accurate enough in view of the fact that the incomes on which the present values have been calculated are estimated figures only. It is, in any event, highly unlikely that an accuracy closer than one per cent will be achieved in practice.

Example 15: If the developer decides to hold the property for 40 years, at which time it is expected to be demolished, what will the internal rate of return (yield) be?

Answer: This is similar to Example 6 where the balance of the income attributable to the building was found to be $90,000 per year when the return required on the land was discounted at 10%, and the yield was found to be less than ten per cent. The rates which will be tested are 8% and 10%. Note that when calculating the present value at 8% the return on the land is discounted at 8% leaving a balance of income attributable to the building of $92,000.

			Present Value @8%	Present Value @10%
Income	$92,000 x YP, 40 years @ 8%			
	= $92,000 x 11.924613	=	$1,097,064	–

$90,000 x YP, 40 years @ 10%

= $90,000 x 9.779051 = – 880,115

Present value of the land	100,000	100,000
Total Present Value	$1,197,064	$980,115

Present value ratio

$$\frac{1,197,064}{1,000,000} \qquad \frac{980,115}{1,000,000}$$

$$= 1.197064 \qquad = 0.980115$$

$$IRR = L\% + \frac{HR - 1.0}{HR - LR}(H\% - L\%)$$

$$= 8\% + \frac{1.197064 - 1.0}{1.197064 - 0.980115} \times (10 - 8)$$

$$= 8\% + \frac{0.197064}{0.216949} \times 3$$

$$= 8\% + 1.816685$$

$$= 9.82\%$$

The internal rate of return (yield) is, say, 9.75%

Example 16: What will be the internal rate of return for the development shown in Table 7 over ten years if the developer intends to sell it for $1,250,00 after five years and expects to be able to obtain a yield of 10% for the next five years?

Answer: This is identical to Example 11, except that now the internal rate of return has to be found. Example 11 showed that the yield was less than 12% so the rate will be tested at 10% and 12%.

		Present Value @10%	Present Value @12%
Income	$100,000 x YP, 5 years @ 10%		
	= $100,000 x 3.790787 =	$379,079	–
	$100,000 x YP, 5 years @ 12%		
	= $100,000 x 3.604776 =	–	360,478
Sale	$1,250,000 x V, 5 years @ 10%		
	= $1,250,000 x 0.620921 =	776,152	–

$1,250,000 x V, 5 years @ 12%

= $1,250,000 x 0.567427 = – 709,284
_____ _____

Total Present Value $1,155,230 $1,069,762

Future value in five years time:

$1,069,761 x A, 5 years @ 12%

= $1,069,762 x 1.762342 = – $1,885,286
========

Future value ten years from now:

$1,885,286 x A, 5 years @ 10%

= $1,885,286 x 1.610510 = – $3,036,272
========

Present value: $3,036,272 x V, 10 years @ 12%

= $3,036,272 x 0.321973 = – $977,598
_____ _____

Total Present Value $1,155,230 $977,598
======= =======

Present value ratio

$$\frac{1,155,230}{1,000,000} \qquad \frac{977,598}{1,000,000}$$

$$= 1.15523 \qquad = 0.977598$$

$$IRR = L\% + \frac{HR - 1.0}{HR - LR}(H\% - L\%)$$

$$= 10\% + \frac{1.15523 - 1.0}{1.15523 - 0.9776} \times (12 - 10)$$

$$= 10\% + \frac{0.15523}{0.1776} \times 2$$

$$= 10\% + 1.7478$$

$$= 11.75\%$$

Note that since a yield of 10% is expected over the last five years there is no need to calculate future values and discount them to a present value for the final five years at 10%.

MODIFIED INTERNAL RATE OF RETURN

As with the present value calculations described earlier, solving for the internal rate of return makes the implicit assumption that the income derived from the investment will be reinvested at the same rate as the yield. In Examples 11 and 16 it was shown how to calculate the present value and internal rate of return when a different rate had to be used for reinvestment, but this applied only to reinvestment at the end of the investment. No allowance was made for any variation in the reinvestment rate on income earned during the investment period but for most real estate calculations the examples shown so far will give a reasonable approximation of the yield, particularly if the internal rate of return is found to be within a realistic borrowing and lending range.

CONSTRUCTION BUDGETING

A further problem can arise if there are a number of negative as well as positive cash flows during the investment period. Changes from positive to negative cash flows, and vice versa, can produce more than one answer. While the answers may be mathematically correct, a multitude of answers are meaningless as a means of determining the yield. In such cases, or if the internal rate of return is found to be outside a realistic borrowing and lending range, a modified internal rate of return can be calculated.

The modified internal rate of return requires two rates – a "safe" rate which is applied to the negative cash flows, and a "reinvestment rate" which is applied to the positive cash flows. A safe rate would be one which is currently paid on short-term GICs while a reinvestment rate would be a rate which could be expected on an investment which has a risk similar to that of the development.

All positive cash flows are compounded forward at the assumed reinvestment rate to give a future value, and the negative cash flows are capitalized at the assumed safe rate to find their present value. The modified internal rate of return is then found using the following formula:

$$\text{MIRR} = 100 \times \left[\left(\frac{\text{FVP}}{\text{PVN}} \right)^{\frac{1}{n}} - 1 \right]$$

where MIRR = the modified internal rate of return
            n   = the number of compounding periods (years)
           FVP = the future value of positive cash flows
and   PVN = the present value of negative cash flows

Example 17: A developer has a development which has a total capital cost of $1,000,000 with no mortgage and which is expected to be sold for $1,600,000 after five years. The anticipated net income is as follows:

Year		
1	$20,000	loss
2	$5,000	loss
3	$75,000	
4	$100,000	
5	$120,000	

What will the modified internal rate of return be?

Answer: The capital cost is a negative cash flow, as are the losses for the first two years, and these will be capitalized to present values using a safe rate of 8%. In the following years the cash flows are all positive, including the sale, and these will be compounded forward at a reinvestment rate of 10% to give future values, as follows:

Year	Net Cash Flow	V @ 8%	A @ 10%		Present Values	Future Values
Capital cost	(1,000,000)				1,000,000	
1	(20,000) x	0.92593		=	18,519	
2	(5,000) x	0.85734		=	4,287	
3	75,000 x		1.21000	=		90,750
4	100,000 x		1.10000	=		110,000
5	120,000			=		120,000

5 (Sale)   1,600,000   =   1,600,000

Totals $1,022,806 $1,920,750

$$MIRR = 100 \times \left(\frac{1,920,750}{1,022,805} \right)^{\frac{1}{5}} - 1$$

$$= 100 \times (1.877924^{0.2} - 1)$$

$$= 100 \times (1.13432 - 1)$$

$$= 13.432\%$$

The modified internal rate of return is, say, 13.50%.

Note that for the negative cash flows the compounding periods increase each year as the present values are computed, whereas for the positive cash flows the compounding periods reduce each year as the future values are computed.

A Small Office Building

Table 9 shows a pro-forma for a small office building development which has an irregular cash flow income. Periodic renovations are expected to occur every five years and periodic repairs every ten years, and the net annual income is reduced for the first twenty-five years by the amount of the mortgage repayments. If the developer were to hold the development for more than twenty-five years the income would increase by $72,767 a year beyond that time.

On the assumption that the developer will expect to sell the development at the end of ten years, the cash flow during the term of the investment would be:

Year   1 $161,760 - $142,567   = $19,193
       2    $161,760 - $142,567   = $19,193
       3    $161,760 - $142,567   = $19,193
       4    $161,760 - $142,567   = $19,193
       5    $161,760 - $142,567 - $4,000   = $15,193
       6    $161,760 - $142,567   = $19,193
       7    $161,760 - $142,567   = $19,193
       8    $161,760 - $142,567   = $19,193
       9    $161,760 - $142,567   = $19,193
      10    $161,760 - $142,567 - $4,000 - $3,000 = $12,193

Since the developer expects to sell the development before the mortgage has expired, the balance of the mortgage principal will have to be calculated as was done in Example 13. On a mortgage of $630,000 at eleven per cent with an amortization period of twenty-five years, the principal repayments at the end of ten years will be $89,217, so the remaining balance will be $540,783. If the expected sale price at the end of ten years is $950,000, the developer's income from the sale, assuming the mortgage can be discharged, will be:

	Sale Price	$950,000
Less	Balance of mortgage	540,783
	Net proceeds of the sale	$409,217

PRO-FORMA FOR A SMALL OFFICE BUILDING

Capital Cost

1.	Land	$60,000
2.	Demolition	3,000
3.	Construction and site works	600,000
4.	Land surveys	1,500
5.	Soil tests	1,500
6.	Market studies	4,000
7.	Appraisal fees	-
8.	Design fees	48,000
9.	Special consultants' fees	-
10.	Legal fees	8,000
11.	Accounting fees	-
12.	Underwriter's fees	-
13.	Developer's fee	10,000
14.	Project management fee	-
15.	Furnishings	-
16.	Artwork	-
17.	Municipal levies	-
18.	Parking levies	-
19.	Capital taxes	-
20.	Real estate taxes	2,500
21.	Insurance	-
22.	Mortgage insurance	-
23.	Performance bonds	-
24.	Maintenance costs	-
25.	Accommodation	-
26.	Developer's administrative costs	3,000
27.	Leasing commissions	16,000
28.	Advertising and public relations	2,000
29.	Tenant inducements	18,000
30.	Tenant lease takeovers	-
31.	Interim lender commitment fees	-
32.	Long-term lender standby fees	-
33.	Brokerage commission	6,500
34.	Registration fees	-
35.	Interim finance	36,000
36.	Initial occupancy costs	-
37.	Contingencies	10,000
		$830,000
38.	Income during construction	-
	Total capital cost	$830,000

Table 9

PRO-FORMA FOR A SMALL OFFICE BUILDING (Continued)

Gross Annual Income

Office space	1,115m² @ $96.86	$108,000
Ground floor space	372m² @ $129.03	48,000
Parking	12 No. @ $480.00	5,760
		$161,760

Annual Expenses

1.	Real estate taxes	$22,000
2.	Insurance	6,000
3.	Cleaning and supplies	12,000
4.	Hydro	4,500
5.	Fuel	2,500
6.	Water	1,000
7.	Security	-
8.	Operating staff	5,000
9.	Service contracts	4,700
10.	Supplies	1,500
11.	Building management	-
12.	Garbage removal	-
13.	Snow removal	500
14.	Gardening	-
15.	Land rental	-
16.	Preventative maintenance	-
17.	Vacancy allowance	8,100
18.	Legal and audit	2,000
19.	Communication equipment	-
20.	Finance costs ($630,000 @ 11% for 25 years)	72,767
		$142,567

Periodic Expenses

1.	Redecoration	$4,000 every 5 years
2.	Repairs	$3,000 every 10 years

Owner's Equity

Total capital cost	$830,000
Less Mortgage	630,000
	$200,000

Table 9 (Concluded)

CONSTRUCTION BUDGETING

With the incomes shown for this development it is difficult to determine the target rates for calculating the internal rate of return. Using a simple capitalization method with the owner's equity of $200,000 as the capital cost and taking $19,000 as the average income, a target rate might be:

$$\frac{\$19,000}{200,000} \times 100 = 9.50\%$$

But this ignores the large income the developer will receive as a result of the sale at the end of ten years, so target rates of ten and fifteen per cent will be assumed.

Year	Income	Present Value @ 10%	Present Value @ 15%
1	$19,193	$17,448	$16,690
2	$19,193	$15,862	$14,513
3	$19,193	$14,420	$12,620
4	$19,193	$13,109	$10,974
5	$15,193	$9,434	$7,554
6	$19,193	$10,834	$8,298
7	$19,193	$9,849	$7,215
8	$19,193	$8,954	$6,274
9	$19,193	$8,140	$5,456
10	$12,193	$4,701	$3,014
10 (Sale)	$409,217	$157,771	$101,152
Total Present Value		$270,522	$193,760

Present value ratio

$$\frac{270,522}{200,000} \qquad \frac{193,760}{200,000}$$

$$= 1.35261 \qquad = 0.96880$$

The internal rate of return is therefore between ten and fifteen per cent, and nearer to fifteen per cent than to ten per cent. At this point with the help of a computer or a financial calculator the actual rate could be found by repeatedly testing at different rates until the present value ratio equals one, or until the present value equals the owner's equity.

Alternatively a third rate, say fourteen per cent, can be tried and if its present value ratio is found to exceed one, the actual rate can be interpolated between fourteen and fifteen per cent:

Year	Income	Present Value @ 14%
1	$19,193	$16,836
2	$19,193	$14,768
3	$19,193	$12,955
4	$19,193	$11,364
5	$15,193	$7,891

6	$19,193	$8,744
7	$19,193	$7,670
8	$19,193	$6,728
9	$19,193	$5,902
10	$12,193	$3,289
10 (Sale)	$409,217	$110,384

Total Present Value $206,531

Present value ratio
$$\frac{206,531}{200,000}$$

$$= 1.03266$$

It appears that the internal rate of return is between fourteen and fifteen per cent:

$$IRR = L\% + \frac{HR - 1.0}{HR - LR} (H\% - L\%)$$

$$= 14\% + \frac{1.03266 - 1.0}{1.03266 - 0.9688} \times (15 - 14)$$

$$= 14\% + \frac{0.03266}{0.06386} \times 1$$

$$= 14\% + 0.51143$$

$$= 14.51\%$$

The internal rate of return (yield) is, say, 14.50%.

If the developer were to hold the development for, say, forty years, at the end of which time the building were to be demolished, a cash flow covering forty years might have to be prepared similar to the example just given. This would certainly have to be done if taxation were included in the calculations but, since taxes are not a factor in the present examples there is, fortunately, a shorter way of finding the internal rate of return over forty years.

This involves separating the net income for the first twenty-five years from the net income for the final fifteen years when mortgage payments are no longer required, and treating the periodic expenses as negative income. The net income for the final fifteen years is discounted back to give a present value in twenty-five years' time, and then this sum is further discounted back to give a present value today. The present value factors for the periodic expenses for each of the years in which they occur are totalled so as to find their present value. The following example should make this clear.

Assume target rates of ten and twelve per cent:

	Present Value @ 10%	Present Value @ 12%
Income for the first 25 years:		
$19,193 x YP, 25 years @ 10%		
= $19,193 x 9.077040 =	174,216	–

$19,193 x YP, 25 years @ 12%

= $19,193 x 7.843139 =   –   150,533

Income for the final 15 years:

$91,960 x YP, 15 years @ 10%

= $91,960 x 7.60608 = $699,455

$699,455 x V, 25 years @ 10%

= $699,455 x 0.092296 =   64,557   –

$91,960 x YP, 15 years @ 12%

= $91,960 x 6.810864 = $626,327

$626,327 x V, 25 years @ 12%

= $626,327 x 0.058823 =   –   36,843

Periodic expenses:

Year	10%		12%	
5	0.6209	-	0.5674	-
10	0.3855	0.3855	0.3220	0.3220
15	0.2394	-	0.1827	-
20	0.1486	0.1486	0.1037	0.1037
25	0.0923	-	0.0588	-
30	0.0573	0.0573	0.0334	0.0334
35	0.0356	-	0.0189	-
	1.5796	0.5914	1.2869	0.4591

Periodic redecorations

$4,000 x 1.5796 =   (6,318)   –

$4,000 x 1.2869 =   –   (5,148)

Periodic repairs

$3,000 x 0.5914 =   (1,774)   –

$3,000 x 0.4591 =   –   (1,377)

Residual land value

$60,000 x V, 40 years @ 10%

= $60,000 x 0.02209 =   1,326   –

$60,000 x V, 40 years @ 12%

= $60,000 x 0.01075 =   –   645

Total Present Value $232,007 $181,496

Present value ratio

$$\frac{232,007}{200,000} \qquad \frac{181,496}{200,000}$$

$$= 1.16004 \qquad = 0.90748$$

$$\text{IRR} = L\% + \frac{HR - 1.0}{HR - LR}(H\% - L\%)$$

$$= 10\% + \frac{1.16004 - 1.0}{1.16004 - 0.90748} \times (12 - 10)$$

$$= 10\% + \frac{0.16004}{0.25256} \times 2$$

$$= 10\% + 1.26734$$

$$= 11.26734\%$$

The internal rate of return (yield) is, say, 11.25%.

COMPUTERS

The calculations in this chapter can all be done with the aid of a personal computer. Most spreadsheet programs have an exponential function which enables the formulae given in the last chapter to be manually entered for the spreadsheet to calculate them. Many spreadsheets also have built-in functions to calculate present and future values and the internal rate of return. Anyone with a little programming knowledge should have no difficulty in writing their own computer program which would not only calculate present and future values, but would also cycle through a series of interest rates until it finds the internal rate of return. This gives a better answer than calculating two rates and interpolating the answer between them as has been done here.

INFLATION

It was mentioned earlier in this chapter that a number of assumptions have to be made when calculating the yield on an investment property. One of the assumptions which might be made is the inflation of income due to increased rental rates in the future. However, coupled with increased rentals is likely to be increases in operating costs. It is usual therefore to base the yield analysis on the known, or reasonably assumed, facts at a particular point in time, usually the time when construction is completed and the building is available for rent, and to ignore any possible future inflation.

CHAPTER 11

Taxation

Although taxation has not been included in any of the yield calculations shown in the last chapter, this is not to say that it is not of great concern to the investor. The inclusion of the taxman as a partner in an investment gives an added dimension to the calculations, invariably reducing the yield, and possibly in some instances making a marginally profitable investment into a decidedly unprofitable one.

The way in which taxes are to be calculated and the actual rate of tax are subject to change from time to time, but the manner of incorporating them into a present value calculation will remain basically the same regardless of any revisions to tax legislation which may be made by governments in the future. A description of the full ramifications of taxation would require a book to itself and this chapter can only give a general outline of the tax implications. The examples given later should be looked upon as showing the method of incorporating taxes into the calculations rather than reflecting the current tax rates which should be used. Before doing these calculations for a proposed development a tax consultant or chartered accountant should be consulted to ensure that the current tax requirements applicable to the development are followed.

CORPORATIONS TAX

Anyone who initiates a building development will normally do so through a corporation rather than as an individual because this has certain legal and tax advantages. Either an existing development company will be used or, if the project is large enough, a new company may be incorporated expressly for the development.

Under the Federal Income Tax Act the federal government levies taxes on all Canadian residents and non-residents, whether corporations or individuals, carrying on business in Canada. In addition, each of the provinces has its own act which imposes taxes on its residents, and on non-residents who have a business establishment there.

The current federal tax rate on a corporation is about thirty-eight per cent, which is reduced by ten per cent for corporations paying provincial taxes. The provincial tax on a corporation varies from ten to seventeen per cent, depending upon the province, making the effective annual tax rate, including both federal and provincial taxes, somewhere between thirty-eight and forty-five per cent.

In most instances taxpayers file tax returns with the federal government for both federal and provincial taxes. The federal government then collects both taxes and passes on the provinces' portion to them. The exceptions to this are corporations within Ontario, Alberta and Quebec which must file separate provincial tax returns.

SMALL BUSINESS DEDUCTION

The Income Tax Act permits a Canadian-controlled private corporation to reduce, under certain conditions, the percentage of tax which would otherwise be payable. The amount of the reduction varies from twenty-one to twenty-three per cent depending on the province. In Ontario, for example, where the normal total business income tax, federal and provincial, would amount to forty-five per cent, the reduction would be twenty-two per cent, making the effective tax rate twenty-three per cent, which is less than most people's personal tax rate, a good reason to incorporate a development company.

A Canadian-controlled private corporation is defined by the act as one which is not a public corporation, which is not controlled directly or indirectly by one or more public corporations, nor by one or more non-resident persons or corporations, and which in most cases is incorporated and resident in Canada.

The small business deduction is allowed only on income from an active business carried on in Canada and not on investment or property income. A development company which maintains a management office and a number of full-time management staff while deriving income from the rental of a building might be considered to be carrying on an active business (as distinct from carrying on an investment or property business) and could, therefore, take advantage of the small business deduction. A corporation set up by someone to manage a couple of houses they owned, on the other hand, would probably not qualify since Revenue Canada would likely consider the income to be investment income.

The rules governing the small business deduction are subject to change periodically but currently the maximum amount on which the deduction may be calculated is $200,000 in any one year. This means that if the taxable income during the year is $200,000 or less the effective tax rate in Ontario, for example, can be reduced to twenty-three per cent. However, if it is more than $200,000 the deduction can only be taken on $200,000, the balance being taxed at the full rate of forty-five per cent. In addition, some provinces increase the rate on income above $200,000 incrementally to a point where the full rate of forty-five per cent is paid on the total income. It is therefore advisable for a corporation which wishes to be eligible for the small business deduction to reduce its taxable income to ensure that it is no more than $200,000. In many cases a private corporation will issue bonuses to its employees to do this rather than pay tax at 45%.

CAPITAL COST ALLOWANCE

The capital cost of a new building is not deductible as an expense for tax purposes but, as with many other assets, depreciation is allowed in the form of a capital cost allowance over the life of the asset. The Federal Income Tax Act has established various classes of depreciable assets, each of which can be depreciated at a differing rate annually by means of a capital cost allowance. Most buildings acquired after 1971 are included in one class, but every rental property with a capital cost of more than $50,000 must be kept separate so that the capital cost allowance can be applied to each individual building. This is to facilitate the adjustment of the capital cost allowance when a corporation which owns several buildings decides to sell one of them.

The capital cost allowance, currently 4% for most buildings, is claimed on the diminishing balance method, which means that the depreciation rate is applied each year to the original cost of the building less the accumulated total of capital cost allowances claimed in previous years. While this is the method used for tax purposes there are other ways in which a company can allow for depreciation, so the capital cost allowance is not necessarily the same as the amount of depreciation carried in the company's books. The difference between the original capital cost and the total capital cost allowances claimed is known as the undepreciated capital cost.

If the property is subsequently sold for a price which is more than the undepreciated capital cost, then the difference between the two is added to taxable income, or recaptured, for that year, subject to a maximum of the capital cost allowance claimed in previous years. In addition, if the proceeds of the sale exceed the original capital cost, a capital gain results, three-quarters of which must be added to taxable income.

If the property is subsequently sold for a price which is less than the undepreciated capital cost, then the difference between the two is deducted from taxable income for that year as a terminal loss.

It should be noted that the capital cost allowance in any one year cannot exceed the net rental income from all the rental buildings in one ownership unless the owner is a corporation whose principal business is holding, developing or selling real estate. This is to prevent taxpayers, particularly individuals in high tax brackets, from investing in depreciable real estate and using the capital cost allowance as a means of reducing tax on other sources of income.

INTERNAL RATE OF RETURN

With a knowledge of the basis of taxation, and the tax rate to be used, it only remains for cash flows incorporating taxes to be set up so that the yield can be calculated. Although tax laws may be liable to change in the future, the developer has to use the current law as the basis for the calculations in a feasibility study.

Example 1: What is the internal rate of return for the development shown in Table 7 if the developer is located in Ontario and expects to sell the development after ten years for $1,500,000, assuming that the development will be done through a corporation and that taxes have to be included in the calculations?

Answer: This is similar to Example 14 in the last chapter except that taxes now have to be included. With a net annual income of $100,000 the development is eligible for the small business deduction which means that the total effective tax rate will be 23%.

In Example 14 the total present value could be found with comparative ease, but now that taxes have to be included a cash flow schedule has to be set up as follows:

Year	Net Income $	Capital Cost Allowance $	Taxable Income $	Tax Payable $	After Tax Cash Flow $
1	100,000	18,000	82,000	18,860	81,140
2	100,000	35,280	64,720	14,886	85,114
3	100,000	33,869	66,131	15,210	84,790
4	100,000	32,514	67,486	15,522	84,478
5	100,000	31,213	68,787	15,821	84,179
6	100,000	29,965	70,035	16,108	83,892
7	100,000	28,766	71,234	16,384	83,616
8	100,000	27,616	72,384	16,648	83,352
9	100,000	26,511	73,489	16,902	83,098
		263,734			
10 (Sale)	1,500,000	(263,734)	263,734		
			375,000		
		638,734	243,100	1,256,900	

This assumes that at the time of the sale the value of the building is still at least $900,000. If the increase in value were all attributable to an increase in the land and the building was now worth less than $900,000, the calculation would be different and the tax payable would be less.

The depreciation rate for the capital cost allowance is taken on $900,000, the capital cost of the building only. Under the current tax law the capital cost allowance is reduced to half the normal rate in the year of acquisition, so in this example it is 2% in the first year and 4% in subsequent years. This assumes that the building will be of masonry or concrete construction. If it were of a different type of construction the depreciation rate could be different.

Because the sale price in Year 10 is more than the unclaimed capital cost, the total of the capital cost allowance has to be included (recaptured) as taxable income in that year. In addition, three-quarters of the difference between the original capital cost of $1,000,000 and the sale price of $1,500,000 also has to be included as taxable income. Assuming no income is earned in year 10 when the building is sold, the taxable income in that year will therefore be the total capital cost allowance of $263,734 to date, plus three-quarters of $500,000, or $375,000, giving a total of $638,734. However, the sale also increases the income for year ten above the allowable $200,000, so the tax payable in Year 10 will be:

$200,000 @ 23% =	$46,000
$638,000 - $200,000 = $438,000 @ 45% =	$197,100
	————
	$243,100
	======

Because the developer is intending to hold the building for ten years it should be possible to claim that it was intended for rental purposes and not for resale. If it had been built with the intention of being sold the developer would have to pay tax on the full difference between the capital cost and the proceeds of the sale. This would apply even if, due to market conditions, the developer were unable to sell and had to rent it for a year or two.

Having established the after-tax cash flow the internal rate of return can be calculated using the procedure described in the last chapter. Example 14 gave an internal rate of return of 12.82%, but now that tax has been incorporated the rate is bound to be somewhat lower. The two rates to be tested will therefore be eight per cent and ten per cent.

Year	Income	Present Value @ 8%	Present Value @ 10%
1	$81,140	$75,130	$73,764
2	$85,114	$72,972	$70,342
3	$84,790	$67,309	$63,704
4	$84,478	$62,094	$57,700
5	$84,179	$57,291	$52,269
6	$83,892	$52,866	$47,355
7	$83,616	$48,789	$42,908
8	$83,352	$45,032	$38,884
9	$83,098	$41,570	$35,242
10	$1,256,900	$582,188	$484,589
		————	————
Total Present Value		$1,105,241	$966,757
		======	======

Present value ratio

$$\frac{1,105,241}{1,000,000} \qquad \frac{966,757}{1,000,000}$$

$$= 1.105241 \qquad = 0.966757$$

$$IRR = L\% + \frac{HR - 1.0}{HR - LR} (H\% - L\%)$$

$$= 8\% + \frac{1.10524 - 1.0}{1.10524 - 0.96676} \times (10 - 8)$$

$$= 8\% + \frac{0.10524}{0.13848} \times 2$$

$$= 8\% + 1.51993$$

$$= 9.52\%$$

The internal rate of return (yield) is, say, 9.5%.

Comparison with the yield found for Example 14 in the last chapter shows that the effect of taxation has been to reduce the yield by more than three per cent.

When a mortgage is used to help finance the project the calculations are essentially the same, but become a little more complicated.

Example 2: What is the internal rate of return for the development shown in Table 8 in Chapter 10 if the developer is located in Ontario and expects to sell the development after ten years for $1,500,000, assuming that the development will be done through a corporation and that taxes have to be included in the calculations?

Answer: This will be tackled in the same way as Example 1, assuming the same tax rate and starting with a cash flow schedule, although the schedule will now have to incorporate the mortgage payments in it as follows:

Year	Principal Repayment $	Net Income $	Mortgage Balance $	Capital Cost Allowance $	Taxable Income $	Tax Payable $	After Tax Cash Flow $
1	6,260	19,632	743,740	18,000	1,632	375	12,997
2	6,967	20,339	736,773	20,339	–	–	13,372
3	7,755	21,127	729,018	21,127	–	–	13,372
4	8,631	22,003	720,387	22,003	–	–	13,372
5	9,606	22,978	710,781	22,978	–	–	13,372
6	10,693	24,065	700,088	24,065	–	–	13,372
7	11,901	25,273	688,187	25,273	–	–	13,372
8	13,246	26,618	674,941	26,618	–	–	13,372
9	14,743	28,115	660,198	26,511	1,604	369	13,003
				206,914			
10 (Sale)		1,500,000	660,198	(206,914)	206,914		
					375,000		
					581,914	217,861	621,941

The net income of $13,372 shown in Table 8 was arrived at by deducting the mortgage repayments of $86,628 each year. While that portion of the mortgage repayment which relates to interest can be claimed as a tax deduction, that portion relating to the principal repayment cannot, so the principal repayment has to be added back as part of the income for tax purposes to give the net incomes shown. This means that in Year 1, for example, the net income is $13,372 plus the mortgage principal repayment of $6,260, giving $19,632. This figure increases each year as more of the repayment is used to pay off the principal and less to pay interest. The after-tax cash flow is the actual net income of $13,372 each year less the tax payable.

In this example, the four per cent capital cost allowance deduction in years 2 - 8 exceed the net income, which would give a negative taxable income. This is not permitted for rental income, although it would be allowed if the building had been built with the intention of selling it, so the capital cost allowance in these years has to equal the net income making the taxable income zero. This has the effect of reducing the total capital cost allowance so that when the building is sold the taxable income is less than it would have been if the full capital cost allowance had been able to be claimed.

The calculation of the taxable income when the property is sold is done in the same way as in Example 1, but the calculation of the tax payable is as follows:

$200,000 @ 23% =	$46,000
$581,914 - $200,000 = $381,914 @ 45% =	171,861
	$217,861

From this, the after tax cash flow will be:

Proceeds of the sale	$1,500,000
Less Mortgage balance	660,198
	$839,802
Less Tax payable	217,861
	$621,941

Because the income is constant for eight years, unlike the income in Example 1, the calculation of the internal rate of return is comparatively simple. Using target rates of twelve and fourteen per cent:

	Present Value @ 12%	Present Value @ 14%
Income $13,372 p.a. for 9 years	71,249	66,143
Adjustment for Year 1, $375	(335)	(329)
Adjustment for Year 9, $369	(133)	(113)
Sale $621,941 in 10 years	200,248	167,765
Total Present Value	$271,029	$233,466

CONSTRUCTION BUDGETING

Present value ratio

$$\frac{271,029}{250,000} \qquad \frac{233,466}{250,000}$$

$$= 1.08412 \qquad = 0.93386$$

$$\text{IRR} = L\% + \frac{HR - 1.0}{HR - LR}(H\% - L\%)$$

$$= 12\% + \frac{1.08412 - 1.0}{1.08412 - 0.93386} \times (14 - 12)$$

$$= 12\% + \frac{0.08412}{0.15026} \times 2$$

$$= 12\% + 1.11966$$

$$= 13.11966\%$$

The internal rate of return (yield) is, say, 13%.

THE GOODS AND SERVICES TAX

The Goods and Services Tax (GST) replaced the existing federal manufacturers' sales tax on 1st January 1991. The GST is calculated at 7% on supplies of all goods and services unless they are otherwise exempt or zero-rated, and generally is payable by the supplier at the time an invoice is issued or becomes payable. The suppliers collect the tax as agents of the federal government but, provided they are registered, are entitled to claim a credit for any taxes they have paid on purchases in connection with their business.

Generally, any person, corporation, partnership or association conducting a commercial activity in Canada where the taxable supplies in the preceding twelve months exceed $30,000 is required to register with Revenue Canada for the purpose of collecting and remitting GST on their sales. For GST purposes a commercial activity includes any activity involving the supply of real estate that is subject to GST and includes non-profit organizations.

Registrants are required, during each reporting period, to remit the excess of tax collected or collectible over any tax credits they may have, or can claim back the excess of any tax credits over the tax collected or collectible. Registered suppliers of goods and services therefore act as unpaid collectors of the tax and the burden of administering and accounting for it falls on them. The additional cost of administering it, as well as any additional financing costs for those businesses which experience adverse cash flow problems as a result of GST, have to be passed on to customers.

The following is an example of how GST is charged and credited over a series of transactions:

	Basic Cost	Net GST Payable
A logging company cuts down a tree and sells it to a sawmill for $100. The logging company adds 7% to its invoice for GST, and pays this amount to the government.	$100	$7.00
The sawmill processes the tree and sells it to a dealer for $250. The sawmill adds 7% to its invoice for GST, but it pays the government the difference between this amount and the GST it has been charged by the logging company ($17.50 - $7.00).	250	10.50

The dealer sells the lumber to a contractor for $300.	300	
The dealer adds 7% to its invoice for GST, but it pays the government the difference between this amount and the GST it has been charged by the sawmill ($21.00 - $17.50).		3.50
The contractor includes $350 for the lumber in its monthly progress draw to the developer.	350	
The contractor adds 7% to its invoice for GST, but it pays the government the difference between this amount and the GST it has been charged by the dealer ($24.50 - $21.00).		3.50
The developer sells the building to a purchaser, including $500 for the lumber.	500	
The developer adds 7% for GST to the invoice, but pays the government the difference between this amount and the GST charged by the contractor ($35.00 - $24.50).		10.50
Total final cost	$500	$35.00

It can be seen that, despite all the transactions which have taken place, the total GST paid is $35, which is 7% of the final selling price. It is actually paid by the final purchaser, but the government has received a series of advances throughout the process. While the purchaser pays the GST in each transaction, it pays it to the seller as part of its bill and it is then up to the seller to submit the GST it has charged to the government. So, while the purchaser "pays" the GST, it is the seller who "pays" it to the government. The seller is obligated to pay the GST at the time it issues an invoice (or at least during its current reporting period), and this means that the seller will be financing the GST if the purchaser doesn't pay its bills promptly. In order to claim a GST refund a purchaser must (in most cases) be a GST registrant who pays GST on behalf of purchasers in subsequent sales. In this example it is assumed that the final purchaser is not qualified to claim a refund. If the final purchaser had been qualified, it would claim the $35 back from the government in the course of its business.

Exemptions

Several components of the development cost of a building are exempt from GST. These include:

Building permits.
Interest on loans.
Insurance.
Bonds.
Mortgage brokerage fees.
Property taxes.
Residential rents, provided the unit is occupied by the same tenant for at least one month, or the rent does not exceed $20 per day or $140 per week.
The lease of land for a building, or the lease of a building which is intended for residential use.

Sale of used residential property.

Sale or lease of residential parking spaces.

Condominium common element fees.

Standard municipal services for property owners such as the installation of roads and sidewalks, and installation and maintenance of water distribution, sewerage and drainage systems in a particular geographic area.

Gas and electrical distribution systems are not exempt.

Residential Construction

Residential rents are not subject to GST, which means that the developer of a building intended to be rented for residential use will not charge GST to the tenants. Unlike the developer of a building intended to be rented for commercial use, which is required to charge GST to its tenants, the developer of a residential building will therefore not be able to claim a refund on any of its expenditures.

There are a number of other requirements concerning the GST and residential property which need to be checked when considering this type of development. These include the special situation of non-profit organizations; the way in which mixed residential and commercial spaces in the same building are handled; the fact that the sale of a new residential complex or a building which has been substantially renovated is subject to tax, whereas the sale of a used building or one which has not been substantially renovated is not; the fact that credits are available to the purchasers of some houses and condominium units and on the purchase of shares in a co-operative housing corporation; and the special self-supply rule which applies to an owner/builder who constructs a residential complex for subsequent lease to tenants.

Tenders and Progress Payments

The Canadian Construction Association recommends that owners include wording in the tender documents instructing bidders not to include GST in their bid. The Goods and Services Tax will, however, be added to the monthly progress payments so that the final contract price will be approximately 7% higher than the bid.

When submitting invoices for progress payments on a stipulated sum contract, each sub-contractor will add 7% for the Goods and Services Tax. The general contractor then has two options for submitting its own progress payment to the client. It can either include the net amount without GST for each sub-contractor, or it can include the amounts of the sub-contractors' invoices with GST included. The following example illustrates this:

A number of sub-contractors have submitted invoices for the current month for formwork, mechanical, electrical etc. totalling	$1,000,000
All have deducted holdbacks, reducing their claims to	$900,000
Also, all have added 7% GST, increasing their claims to	$963,000
In addition, the general contractor is claiming for such items as General Conditions, Fee etc. totalling	$100,000
From which it will deduct holdbacks, reducing its claim to	$90,000

There are two ways to process the claim:

1. Sub-contractors' claims (including GST) $963,000
    General contractor's claim   90,000
    GST on general contractor's claim - 7%   6,300

    Total $1,059,300

2. Sub-contractors' claims (excluding GST) $900,000
    General contractor's claim   90,000

     $990,000
    Add GST - 7%   69,300

    Total $1,059,300

The second method is preferred since it avoids confusion about the amount of GST which has been included in the progress claim and how much the owner can claim as a refund.

CONCLUSION

Tax laws change frequently and a development company and its advisers would be wise to consult an accountant or tax specialist before embarking on a feasibility study incorporating taxation to ensure that the current Department of Revenue requirements are included.

CHAPTER 12

Life-Cycle Costing

One of the objectives given in Chapter 5 for cost control in the pre-tender period of a construction project was to give the building owner value for money. However, cost planning deals primarily with the capital cost and, while this is important, it is only one of the costs associated with a building over its life. Repairs, maintenance, and operating costs continue throughout the life of a building, and buildings generally have a long life over which these costs can be incurred. Value for money should therefore extend beyond capital costs to include these other costs. To make decisions on the basis of capital costs alone, without considering these subsequent costs, can be misleading.

Life-cycle costing, also known as life costing, life-span costing, cost in use, or ultimate costs, is a technique which takes into account the total costs, both present and future. It is a comparative technique used to make decisions between choices and on its own a life-cycle cost is relatively meaningless. It can be used, for example, to help decide whether to renovate an existing building or to demolish it and build a new one, or whether to sell the property and rent accommodation elsewhere. In the early design stages it can be used to help select the most appropriate size and shape of the building, or the best interior planning solution, by comparing not only the capital costs but also the effect of the design on future operating costs. In the later design stages it can be used to make decisions about the choice of systems and materials in the building. Life-cycle costing can therefore be used to make decisions throughout the pre-construction period – from decisions about the building as a whole to decisions about the choice of materials to be incorporated within it.

Life-cycle cost studies will sometimes show that the most economical design is not the one which has the least capital cost and that it may be worth paying more now in order to make savings in running costs during the life of the building. The most economical solution is usually that which has the lowest life-cycle cost, but there may be occasions when the difference is marginal, or when the capital expenditure required for the optimum solution is more than the building owners are is prepared to pay, and they may decide to choose the alternative which has the lower capital cost. Whatever their choice, at least they have made their decisions knowing the probable cost implications on the building throughout its life.

It has been said that value for money spent on a building depends upon the three factors of appearance, function and cost, all three of which are based on judgement. The first is, perhaps, a subjective assessment but nevertheless can be agreed upon between the building owners and their architects. The second must be based on the owner's requirements, while the third has to take into account the other two and strike a proper balance between them and the owner's financial resources. Life-cycle costing enables this to be done over the life of the building.

Balancing cost against appearance will depend upon the owner's objectives. Some owners are prepared to spend more, both in capital and in running costs, on appearance if it enhances the prestige of their building. This may be due to the increased revenue the building can then command, to the greater ease in raising capital for it, to the advertising advantages it gives, or for no good reason except the owner's sense of importance. Estimating the monetary value of the last two of these objectives can sometimes be difficult.

Balancing cost against function will also depend upon the owner's objectives. In the case of a manufacturing plant, the cost of the building can be looked on as being one of the factors of production, with no value in itself except as it contributes to the profitability of the business. Here the objective will be to maximize the profits of the business as a whole, which may not necessarily mean minimizing the capital cost of the building. The life-cycle cost of the building in such a case would then include, as it would for some other types of building such as a health or education facility, the costs associated with the functions being carried on within the building as well as the costs involved in operating the building itself.

The value of a building erected for rental purposes, on the other hand, is related solely to its income potential as a building. It is not just one of the factors of production, it is the only factor of production. It is unlikely that a developer would need to be concerned with the functions being performed within it except insofar as they might affect its income potential, such as its being used for illegal activities. The life-cycle costs of this type of building would not therefore normally need to include the costs of the functions within the building, but only those costs related to the operation of the building.

PRESENT VALUE METHOD

Life-cycle costing requires the accumulation of all the costs associated with whatever aspect of the building is being studied, both present and future, to give a total cost. Since it is a comparative method those costs which are common to both alternatives being studied do not need to be included. A comparison between two types of floor finishes, for example, would not need to include the cost of a topping if the same topping were required for both. Also, life-cycle costing is concerned with the comparison of costs and rarely needs to take income into account. Only if the choice is likely to affect the income of the building does it need to be included in the calculations.

As was made clear in earlier chapters, adding present and future costs together without discounting the future costs will give a misleading answer because expenditures to be made in the future are not the same as current expenditures. The Present Value Method of calculating life-cycle costs is therefore very similar to the method described in Chapter 10 for calculating net present value, in which a discount rate is assumed to find the present value of future expenditures. The discounted values of future expenditures, both annual and periodic, are then added to the capital cost to give a total life-cycle cost. The Present Value Method is not the only way in which life-cycle costs can be analyzed. The Annual Equivalent Method, which will be described later, can also be used and will give the same result in terms of ranking the alternatives, but the Present Value Method is more usual, particularly in North America. This is because it is a comparatively easy technique and in most circumstances provides an adequate answer.

Example 1: Two roofing systems are to be compared. Roof A has a capital cost of $2,000, a life of twenty years, and an estimated repair cost of $200 every ten years. Roof B has a capital cost of $3,500, a life of forty years, and an estimated repair cost of $200 every twenty years. The building is expected to last for forty years, and the discount rate is assumed to be ten per cent. Which is the more economical roof finish?

Answer: Roof A is less expensive than Roof B in capital cost. However, Roof A has to be replaced during the life of the building, and the cost and timing of repairs is given. Assuming that inflation does not need to be included in the calculations, the total costs without discounting would be as follows:

	Roof A	Roof B
Initial Cost	$2,000	$3,500
Repair at the end of 10 years	200	–
Replacement at the end of 20 years	2,000	–
Repair at the end of 20 years	–	200
Repair at the end of 30 years	200	–
Total costs	$4,400	$3,700

This would seem to indicate that Roof B is less expensive over the life of the building, largely because of the replacement cost of Roof A in twenty years' time. If the future expenditures are now discounted to present values the comparison would appear as follows:

	Roof A	Roof B
Initial Cost	$2,000	$3,500
Repair at the end of 10 years:		
$200 x V, 10 years @ 10% = $200 x 0.38554 =	77	–
Replacement at the end of 20 years:		
$2,000 x V, 20 years @ 10% = $2,000 x 0.14864 =	297	–
Repair at the end of 20 years:		
$200 x V, 20 years @ 10% = $200 x 0.14864 =	–	30
Repair at the end of 30 years:		
$200 x V, 30 years @ 10% = $200 x 0.05731 =	11	–
Total present cost	$2,385	$3,530

The indication now is that Roof A not only has a lower capital cost than Roof B but also a lower life-cycle cost and is therefore the more economical. Discounting the cost of replacing Roof A in twenty years has reduced its cost from $2,000 to $297, the principal reason why Roof A has now become less expensive than Roof B. Note that there is no point in repairing or replacing the roofs in year 40 when the building is to be demolished.

In this simple example such variables as the capital costs, the cost of repairs, the discount rate, the life of each roof and the life of the building are given. In practice they are rarely given but have to be assumed and the reasoning behind the assumptions will be dealt with later. It might also be asked why the interest the owner could earn by investing the $1,500 difference in capital costs between the two roofs has not been taken into account. In fact, because this is a present value calculation, the present value of $1,500 invested now has to be $1,500 no matter for how long it is invested nor what discount rate is assumed. Any future investment assumptions are therefore immaterial and there is no need to take them into consideration. Only if it might be thought that the investment would be at a different rate than the one assumed for the study might an adjustment be thought to be necessary, but this is very unlikely.

Example 2: The costs of two heating systems are to be compared. System A has an initial cost of $50,000 and an annual operating and maintenance cost of $4,500. System B has an initial cost of $60,000 and an annual operating and maintenance cost of $3,000. Both systems are expected to last for thirty years and the discount rate is assumed to be ten per cent. Which is the more economical system?

Answer: The following is a comparison between the two systems:

	System A	System B
Initial cost	$50,000	$60,000
Operating and maintenance costs:		
System A: $4,500 x YP, 30 years @ 10%		
= $4,500 x 9.42691 =	42,421	–
System B: $3,000 x YP, 30 years @ 10%		
= $3,000 x 9.42691 =	–	28,281
Total present cost	$92,421	$88,281

Despite its higher initial cost System B has a lower life-cycle cost over thirty years.

Example 3: The costs of two floor finishes are to be compared. Floor A has an initial cost of $10,000, needs replacing every ten years, and costs $1,200 in maintenance every year. Floor B has an initial cost of $15,000, needs replacing every fifteen years, and has a maintenance cost of $800 a year. The building is expected to last forty years, and the discount rate is assumed to be eight per cent. Which is the more economical floor finish?

Answer:

	Floor A	Floor B
Initial cost	$10,000	$15,000
Replacement at the end of 10 years:		
$10,000 x V, 10 years @ 8% = $10,000 x 0.46319 =	4,632	–
Replacement at the end of 15 years:		
$15,000 x V, 15 years @ 8% = $15,000 x 0.31524 =	–	4,729
Replacement at the end of 20 years:		
$10,000 x V, 20 years @ 8% = $10,000 x 0.21455 =	2,145	–
Replacement at the end of 30 years:		
(A) $10,000 x V, 30 years @ 8% = $10,000 x 0.09938 =	994	–
(B) $15,000 x V, 30 years @ 8% = $15,000 x 0.09938 =	–	1,491
Maintenance:		
Floor A: $1,200 x YP, 40 years @ 8%		
= $1,200 x 11.92461 =	14,310	–
Floor B: $800 x YP, 40 years @ 8%		
= $800 x 11.92461 =	–	9,540
Total present cost	$32,081	$30,760

The difference is marginal, the life-cycle cost of Floor B proving to be slightly less than Floor A despite its higher capital cost. The difference is largely accounted for by the difference in maintenance costs and in this instance the building owner would probably be wiser to select floor A because of the fifty per cent premium in the initial cost of Floor B, and also in the hope that the maintenance costs of Floor A might in fact be reduced.

An alternative way of making this calculation, which is slightly shorter, is as follows:

				Floor A	Floor B
Initial cost				$10,000	$15,000
V @ 8%,	10 years =	0.46319	–		
	15 years =	–	0.31524		
	20 years =	0.21455	–		
	30 years =	0.09938	0.09938		
		0.77712	0.41462		
Replacement of Floor A:		$10,000 x 0.77712 =		7,771	–
Replacement of Floor B:		$15,000 x 0.41462 =		–	6,219
Maintenance:					
Floor A: $1,200 x YP, 40 years @ 8%					
= $1,200 x 11.92461 =				14,310	–
Floor B: $800 x YP, 40 years @ 8%					
= $800 x 11.92461 =				–	9,540
Total present cost				$32,081	$30,759

Note that in the replacement cycle in Example 3, Floor A is due to be replaced again in year forty. As with example 1, since the building has been given a life of only forty years there is no point in replacing the floor in the last year of its life.

Present value is a rather imprecise term when used in conjunction with the life-cycle cost of a complete building project. It can mean that point in time when the land is purchased, or the time when construction has been completed and the building is available for occupation, or any point of time in between. Usually it is defined as the time when construction has been completed. If the purpose of the life-cycle cost study is to investigate the effect of the construction time on two alternative design proposals, all expenditures made before completion of construction should be compounded forward to give a terminal value at the date of completion. Normally, however, this is unnecessary because pre-occupancy costs don't usually have any affect on operating and maintenance costs, and anyway they would be expected to be the same for both alternatives.

Example 4 illustrates a situation where expenditures made prior to the completion of construction are compounded forward to give a terminal value at the date of completion so that they can be added to the present value of future expenditures. Land and its associated costs are compounded in their entirety, while the cost of construction is compounded from the mid-point of construction to the date of completion.

Example 4: A site has been purchased for $175,000. One alternative is to erect a building which will cost $5,250,000 to build, will take 12 months to design and 24 months to build, and which will have annual expenses of $640,000 and periodic expenses of $75,000 every 25 years. The other alternative is to erect a building which will cost $5,400,000 to build, which will take 10 months to design and 20 months to build, and which will have annual expenses of $630,000 and periodic expenses of $50,000 every 20 years. Which alternative should be chosen, assuming a 40 year life in both cases and a discount rate of 9%?

Answer: Although the first alternative is a building with a lower construction cost it will take longer to design and build than the other, which is rather unusual. The differences in expenses, particularly the periodic expenses, also make it difficult to make a direct comparison between the two. Life-cycle cost studies are made for each alternative in turn:

Alternative 1
The site will be acquired 3 years before construction is complete. The present value of the site, assuming the completion of construction to be the datum and using the future value factor, will be:

$175,000 x A, 3 years @ 9%	= $175,000 x 1.29503 =	$226,630

The mid-point of construction will be 12 months before construction is complete. The present value of the building, again using the future value factor, will be:

$5,250,000 x A, 1 year @ 9%	= $5,250,000 x 1.09000 =	5,722,500
Design Fees, 8%		420,000
Periodic Expenses, 25 years:		
$75,000 x V, 25 years @ 9%	= $75,000 x 0.11597 =	8,698
Annual expenses, 40 years:		
$640,000 x YP, 40 years @ 9%	= $640,000 x 10.75736 =	6,884,710

Total present cost $13,262,538

Alternative 2
The site will be acquired 2½ years before construction is complete. The present value of the site will have to be calculated by interpolation as follows:

A for 2 years @ 9% =   1.18810
A for 3 years @ 9% =   1.29503

      2.48313

A for 2½ years @ 9% = 1.24156 $175,000 x 1.24156 = $217,273

The mid-point of construction will be 10 months before construction is complete. Interest for one year is 9% so the interest for five-sixths of a year is .09 x 5/6 = 0.075, and A for 10 months will be = 1.075.

The present value of the building will therefore be:

$5,400,000 x A, 10 months @ 9%	= $5,400,000 x 1.075 =	5,805,000
Design Fees, 8%		432,000
Periodic Expenses, 20 years:		
$50,000 x V, 20 years @ 9%	= $50,000 x 0.17843 =	8,922
Annual expenses, 40 years:		
$630,000 x YP, 40 years @ 9%	= $630,000 x 10.75736 =	6,777,137
Total present cost		$13,240,332

Despite an additional capital expenditure of $150,000 for Alternative 2, it is in fact less expensive over a 40 year period than Alternative 1. Part of the reason for this is the difference in the annual expenses for the two alternatives, but by reducing the length of time required for design and construction, Alternative 2 cuts the difference in capital cost from $150,000 to a little over $73,000.

The method of calculating the present value of the site for Alternative 2, by interpolation between the future values for two and three years to give the future value for two and a half years, has to be done when discount tables are the only means available for obtaining Future Worth of One Dollar factors. The result is not completely accurate because there is not a straight line relationship between the factors for two adjacent years, although the resulting error is not enough to nullify the result. Using the formula given in Chapter 9, the actual factor for the Future Worth of One Dollar at nine per cent for two and a half years is found to be 1.24041. This would give a present value for the site of $217,072. Similarly, the factor for the future value of the building over a ten month period should in fact be 1.07446 giving a present value of $5,802,064. Making these corrections to Alternative 2 would have the effect of increasing the difference between the two alternatives.

ANNUAL EQUIVALENT METHOD

Another way of analyzing life-cycle costs is to convert all costs into annual equivalents, using the Annual Equivalent Worth factor described in Chapter 9. Compared to the Present Value Method it has the disadvantage that future periodic expenditures must first be converted to present values before they can be expressed as annual equivalent costs, thus adding to the number of calculations which have to be performed. However, there are occasions when it might give a more meaningful answer, as for example when the cost of owning a building is to be compared with the cost of renting equivalent space elsewhere, since rentals are always expressed as annual expenditures. It might also be used when there are no future periodic expenditures to be considered. As noted earlier, the Present Value Method and the Annual Equivalent Method will both give the same result in terms of ranking the life-cycle costs of different alternatives.

Example 5: Compare the life-cycle costs of the two roofs in Example 1 using the Annual Equivalent Worth method.

Answer: The initial costs can be converted to annual equivalent costs using Annual Equivalent Worth factors, but before this can be done for the repair and replacement costs they must first be expressed at present values. The calculations will be:

	Roof A	Roof B

Initial cost: Roof A $2,000 x AEW, 40 years @ 10%

= $2,000 x 0.10226 = $204.52 —

Roof B $3,500 x AEW, 40 years @ 10%

= $3,500 x 0.10226 = — $357.91

Repair at the end of 10 years:

$200 x V, 10 years @ 10% = $200 x 0.38554 = $77.11

$77.11 x AEW, 40 years @ 10% = $77.11 x 0.10226 = 7.89 —

Replacement at the end of 20 years:

$2,000 x V, 20 years @ 10% = $2,000 x 0.14864 = $297.28

$297.28 x AEW, 40 years @ 10% = $297.28 x 0.10226 = 30.40 —

Repair at the end of 20 years:

$200 x V, 20 years @ 10% = $200 x 0.14864 = $29.73

$29.73 x AEW, 40 years @ 10% = $29.73 x 0.10226 = — 3.04

Repair at the end of 30 years:

$200 x V, 30 years @ 10% = $200 x 0.05731 = $11.46

$11.46 x AEW, 40 years @ 10% = $11.46 x 0.10226 = 1.17 —

Total annual equivalent cost $243.98 $360.95

This is a lengthy calculation when compared with the present value solution found in Example 1. Moreover it can be seen that in each case the present value is first found and then converted to an annual equivalent worth. A far quicker method would be to find the total present cost of each roof as was done in Example 1 and then convert the totals into annual equivalent costs using the Annual Equivalent Worth factor for 40 years at 10%.

Roof A: Total present cost (from Example 1) = $2,385
            Annual equivalent cost = $2,385 x 0.10226 = $243.89

Roof B: Total present cost (from Example 1) = $3,530
            Annual equivalent cost = $3,530 x 0.10226 = $360.98

The slight discrepancy in the figures is due to rounding of the figures in Example 1.

Example 6: Compare the life-cycle costs of the two heating systems in Example 2 using the Annual Equivalent Method.

Answer: This example has no future periodic costs so the calculations will be much simpler than in the previous example:

		System A	System B
Initial cost:	System A $50,000 x AEW, 30 years @ 10% = $50,000 x 0.10608 =	$5,304.00	–
	System B $60,000 x AEW, 30 years @ 10% = $60,000 x 0.10608 =	–	$6,364.80
Annual costs		4,500.00	3,000.00
Total annual equivalent cost		$9,804.00	$9,364.80

Example 7: Compare the life-cycle costs of the two floor finishes in Example 3 using the Annual Equivalent Method.

Answer: In this example capital, periodic and annual costs are given. This could require a lengthy calculation but can be shortened slightly as was done in Example 3 in the following manner:

			Floor A	Floor B
Initial cost:	Floor A $10,000 x AEW, 40 years @ 8% = $10,000 x 0.08386 =		$838.60	–
	Floor B $15,000 x AEW, 40 years @ 8% = $15,000 x 0.08386 =		–	$1,257.90

V @ 8%,		
10 years =	0.46319	–
15 years =	–	0.31524
20 years =	0.21455	–
30 years =	0.09938	0.09938
	0.77712	0.41462

Replacement of Floor A:
  $10,000 x 0.77712 = $7,771.20
  $7,771.20 x AEW, 40 years @ 8% = $7,771.20 x 0.08386 =   651.69   –

Replacement of Floor B:
  $15,000 x 0.41462 = $6,219.30
  $6,219.30 x AEW, 40 years @ 8% = $6,219.30 x 0.08386 =   –   521.55

Maintenance costs	1,200.00	800.00
Total annual equivalent cost	$2,690.29	$2,579.45

Example 8: A small business has a choice between renting space in an existing building or constructing its own office building. If it builds, the following costs are expected:

Cost of the site	$60,000
Other capital costs	$770,000
Annual costs	$142,000
Periodic redecorations	$1,500 every 5 years
Periodic repairs	$3,000 every 10 years

If it rents, the annual rent will be $90.00 per m² for 1,200m², $120.00 per m² for 400m², and 12 parking spaces at $480.00 each. The rental rates include all taxes etc. If the life of the building is assumed to be thirty years and the discount rate is nine per cent which is the better alternative?

Answer: *Alternative 1 - Construct a new building*

1. Land: $60,000 x i = $60,000 x 0.09 = $5,400

2. Other capital costs: $770,000 x AEW, 30 years @ 9%
   = $770,000 x 0.09734 = 74,952

3. Annual costs: 142,000

4. Periodic redecorations:

   V @ 9%   5 years   = 0.64993
              10 years   = 0.42241
              15 years   = 0.27454
              20 years   = 0.17843
              25 years   = 0.11597
                        ————
                       1.64128
                        ====

   $1,500 x 1.64128 = $2,461.92
   $2,461.92 x AEW, 30 years @ 9% = $2,461.92 x 0.09734 = 240

5. Periodic repairs:

   V @ 9%   10 years   = 0.42241
              20 years   = 0.17843
                        ————
                       0.60084
                        ====

   $3,000 x 0.60084 = $1,802.52
   $1,802.52 x AEW, 30 years @ 9% = $1,802.52 x 0.09734 = 175

6. Residual land value at the end of 30 years:
   $60,000 x V, 30 years @ 9% = $60,000 x 0.07537 = $4,522.27
   $4,522.27 x AEW, 30 years @ 9% = $4,522.27 x 0.09734 = (440)

Total annual equivalent cost $222,327

Alternative 2 - Rent

1,200 m² @ $90.00 =	$108,000
400 m² @ $120.00 =	48,000
12 Parking spaces @ $480.00 =	5,760
	———
Total annual equivalent cost	$161,760
	=======

This shows that it would be more economical to rent space than to construct a new building which would certainly be true if inflation does not have to be taken into account. However, although it is highly unlikely that the rental rates will remain constant over the next thirty years, the construction alternative carries major annual costs which would also be subject to inflation and the two could quite possibly offset each other. The question of inflation will be discussed more fully later.

Present Value and Annual Equivalent are not the only ways in which life-cycle costs can be analyzed, although they are the methods most commonly used. There is no reason why they shouldn't be analyzed on Future or Terminal Values except that this has no advantage over the Present Value Method and is, perhaps, less meaningful. Another method which might be appropriate under certain circumstances is to select one of the alternatives and to find its total present value using an assumed discount rate. The other alternative is then analyzed to see what discount rate is needed to give the same present value, in the same way as the internal rate of return was found in Chapter 10. Whichever alternative had the higher discount rate would be the more economical. This method would give the same ranking as the Present Value and the Annual Equivalent methods, but for a complicated life-cycle cost study it is likely that a computer would be needed for the calculations.

DISCOUNT RATES

Because the Present Value and Annual Equivalent methods of life-cycle costing require future costs to be discounted, the appropriate discount rate has to be selected. The rate will obviously have an effect on the life-cycle cost, and although the objective is to compare alternatives, the same rate being used for each, an error in the rate might affect their ranking in some instances. The rate will vary depending on the individual building owners who either have to borrow money to finance their buildings, or sacrifice an alternative use of their own money. The applicable discount rate should therefore be that rate of interest which they could obtain by investing their funds in an investment of equivalent risk and is unlikely to be, for example, the interest rate for the mortgage on the building. In the case of developers putting up income-producing buildings it could be the internal rate of return they expect on their development. In other cases it will have to be found in discussions with the building owners, and could be based on a mix of the average rate of return of their business, their cost of borrowing, and the anticipated rate of inflation. Or it may be a weighted average of the financial sources of their business, both debt and equity. Even the government, while it raises money principally by taxation, has to borrow and has a substantial national debt to be repaid, and any expenditure on building is not available for other purposes, so an appropriate discount rate can be found for government projects as well as for private projects.

The effect of the discount rate on costs can be seen in Table 10 which shows the present values of annual expenditures of a thousand dollars at different interest rates over various periods of time. It can be seen that an increase in the discount rate reduces the amount which has to be paid now to make a given annual saving. Over a fifty year time period, for example, with a discount rate of five per cent, an additional capital expenditure of

$18,256 will be required to provide a saving of $1,000 in annual cost. If the discount rate is increased to twelve per cent the additional capital cost is reduced to $8,304. As the discount rate increases, less needs to be spent now to save future annual costs. From this it follows that as the discount rate is increased in a life-cycle cost study, a lower increase in capital costs appears to be needed to reduce future costs. Conversely, a decrease in the rate will appear to need a higher increase in capital costs to achieve the same saving, making the building more expensive.

Present values of annual expenditures of $1,000

	5%	8%	10%	12%
10 years	7,722	6,710	6,145	5,650
20 years	12,462	9,818	8,514	7,469
30 years	15,372	11,258	9,427	8,055
40 years	17,159	11,925	9,779	8,244
50 years	18,256	12,233	9,915	8,304
60 years	18,929	12,377	9,967	8,324
70 years	19,343	12,443	9,987	8,330
80 years	19,596	12,474	9,995	8,332
90 years	19,752	12,488	9,998	8,333
100 years	19,848	12,494	9,999	8,333

Table 10

Annual equivalent worths of $1,000

	5%	8%	10%	12%
10 years	129.50	149.03	162.75	176.98
20 years	80.24	101.85	117.46	133.38
30 years	65.05	88.83	106.08	124.14
40 years	58.28	83.86	102.26	121.30
50 years	54.78	81.74	100.86	120.42
60 years	52.83	80.80	100.83	120.13
70 years	51.70	80.37	100.13	120.04
80 years	51.03	80.17	100.05	120.01
90 years	50.63	80.08	100.02	120.00
100 years	50.38	80.04	100.01	120.00

Table 11

The same effect can be seen in Table 11 which shows the annual equivalent worths of a thousand dollars invested now at different interest rates over various periods of time. Higher equivalent worths are generated at a higher discount rate than at a lower rate. There is therefore a tendency for high rates to encourage lower capital costs with lower standards of construction because the resulting future operating and maintenance costs are heavily discounted, while low rates tend to encourage higher capital costs and better standards of construction.

TIME

Time is another factor which has to be considered when studying life-cycle costs. It can be considered under two headings: the life of the building itself, and the lives of the materials and components which go into it.

The life of a building very often depends not so much on its physical life as on its economical or functional life. Many buildings are constructed which, given the quality of the materials of which they are made, could be expected to last many hundreds of years, yet because of economic factors or changes in technology they become obsolete and have to be demolished long before their physical life has come to an end. How soon they become obsolete will depend very much on the type of building and its location, and to some extent on its architectural merit. An example of economic obsolescence would be an owner who decides it would be more profitable to demolish the building because a better use for the site has been found. Functional obsolescence would occur if the owner found it to be cheaper to demolish and rebuild rather than try to adapt the building to meet the changing requirements of the business. This makes it difficult to forecast the probable life of a building, although a realistic estimate is needed since it can affect the outcome of the life-cycle costs.

The other aspect of time, that of the life of the materials or components which are used in the building, can be equally difficult to predict. The lives of many materials and components are less than the life of the building and they may be replaced many times during the building's lifetime, either because it is cheaper to replace than to repair them, or because they are not capable of being repaired. Little accurate information is available on the expected lives of materials and components, partly because their lives are dependent to some extent on the maintenance policy of the owner and partly because the amount of use they receive in the building will affect their longevity. A composition tile floor, for example, will last longer in a building which is well maintained, particularly if it is located in an area which does not receive much wear, than it will in a building which is poorly maintained and where the floor is subject to heavy traffic. Enquiries directed to the manufacturers of materials and components are likely to elicit optimistic responses which would lead to unrealistic estimates of a product's durability. A more fruitful source would be property managers and building owners who have had long experience in building maintenance. The problem of predicting the life of a material is made worse when the life-cycle cost of a new material is required. In this case, since no data on past performance will be available, the life of the material will have to be assumed, or alternatively a calculation must be made of the life necessary for the life-cycle cost of the new material to equal that of the material with which it is being compared, and a decision made on the probability of this life expectancy being achieved.

The effect of the assumed life of a building or component is shown in Table 10. Using a five per cent discount rate, if the life expectancy is assumed to be fifty years, $18,256 needs to be added to the capital cost to save a future annual expense of a thousand dollars, whereas if the life expectancy is reduced to twenty years the additional expenditure is reduced to $12,462. Table 11 also shows that, as with increasing the discount rate, assuming a shorter life expectancy increases the annual equivalent worth. Essentially this means that a building or component with a shorter life expectancy should have less spent on it in capital cost than a building with a longer life expectancy, even though this may mean spending more on future operating and maintenance costs. Lowering the life expectancy has the same effect as increasing the discount rate, it encourages lower capital costs and lower standards of construction. However, manufacturers of building materials and components do not produce different products for use in buildings with differing life-spans, and the same products can be used in both short-life and long-life buildings. A building intended to have only a short life is not therefore proportionately less expensive in capital cost than one intended to have a longer life.

Another conclusion which can be drawn from Tables 10 and 11 is that after a certain period of time the life of the building has only a small effect on the present value of future expenditures. At a five per cent discount rate this occurs after about sixty years, beyond which time an increase in the assumed life of the building will have only a minimal effect. At eight per cent it occurs after about fifty years, at ten per cent after forty years, and at twelve per cent after thirty years. One result of this is that any error in predicting future costs in a life-cycle cost study will have a greater effect if the life of the building is underestimated than if it is overestimated. However, the shorter the assumed life of the building the less effect an error in the discount rate will have on the present value. With a life of ten years, the saving of an annual expenditure of a thousand dollars can be accomplished with a capital cost of $7,722 if the discount rate is taken to be five per cent, and $5,650 if the rate is taken to be twelve per cent, a difference of $2,072. With a life expectancy of fifty years the capital costs need to be $18,256 and $8,304 respectively, a difference of $9,951. This means that the accuracy of the discount rate is more important for a long-life building than it is for a short-life building.

INFLATION

Two types of inflation might be considered for inclusion in a life-cycle cost analysis – general inflation in the economy as a whole, and escalation in construction costs. Most authorities agree that general inflation should not be included. All life-cycle cost studies have to be based on assumptions about the future and, as with a financial feasibility study, including general inflation as an additional assumption only increases the possibility of error. Also, interest rates tend to rise during periods of inflation so the two are likely to cancel each other out. In addition, general inflation will affect all costs equally and since life-cycle costing is an exercise in comparative costs, not in absolute costs, its inclusion should not affect the ranking of the alternatives.

If it is decided to include general inflation in a life-cycle cost study this can be accomplished by modifying the discount rate using the following formula:

$$MR = \left(\frac{1 + i}{1 + e} - 1 \right) \times 100$$

where MR = the modified discount rate
  i = the discount rate
and e = the rate of inflation.

This formula reduces the discount rate although a close approximation can be found merely by deducting the anticipated inflation rate from the discount rate to give the modified rate, which is usually close enough in practice. Thus, if a discount rate of ten per cent is to be used and inflation is expected to be four per cent per year, the modified discount rate will be 5.77% if calculated by the formula, and six per cent by simple deduction.

This applies only to the costs which are included in a life-cycle cost study. If a positive cash flow such as income or salvage value has to be included the following formula must be used for modifying the discount rate of the positive cash flows only:

$$MR = [(1 + i)(1 + e) - 1] \times 100$$

This formula increases the discount rate and can also be approximated, this time by adding the anticipated inflation rate to the discount rate to give the modified rate. The reason why different formulas are needed for expenses and income is that inflation will cause future expenses to increase, and future income to decrease in real terms. As can be seen from Table 10, a reduction in the discount rate has the effect of increasing the present value of future costs while an increase in the discount rate reduces the present value of future income.

Although general inflation is not usually included in life-cycle cost studies, escalation in construction costs or in maintenance or operating costs frequently should be included, despite the difficulties of making these predictions. If, for example, two heating systems are being compared and there are indications that the cost of the fuel for one is likely to increase at a higher rate than for the other, this differential should be allowed for in the study. Similarly, when two materials with different lives are being compared and replacement costs will be involved, price escalation should be included because escalation will affect the comparative costs of replacement due to the difference in timing.

Example 9: What will be the life-cycle costs of the two roofs in Example 1 if the rate of escalation in construction costs is expected to be five per cent per annum?

Answer: Escalation can be allowed for in three ways: by using the formula given earlier to modify the discount rate, by deducting the escalation rate from the discount rate, or by allowing for escalation first and then discounting the result. By way of illustration, the third method will be used:

		Roof A	Roof B
Initial cost		$2,000	$3,500

Repair at the end of 10 years:

Escalation:	$200 x A, 10 years @ 5%		
	= $200 x 1.62889 = $326		
Discounted:	$326 x V, 10 years @ 10%		
	= $326 x 0.38554 =	126	–

Replacement at the end of 20 years:

Escalation:	$2,000 x A, 20 years @ 5%		
	= $2,000 x 2.65330 = $5,307		
Discounted:	$5,307 x V, 20 years @ 10%		
	= $5,307 x 0.14864 =	789	–

Repair at the end of 20 years:

Escalation:	$200 x A, 20 years @ 5%		
	= $200 x 2.65330 = $531		
Discounted:	$531 x V, 20 years @ 10%		
	= $531 x 0.14864 =	–	79

Repair at the end of 30 years:

Escalation:	$200 x A, 30 years @ 5%		
	= $200 x 4.32194 = $864		
Discounted:	$864 x V, 30 years @ 10%		
	= $864 x 0.05731 =	50	–

Total present cost		$2,965	$3,579

Including escalation has made no difference to the ranking of the alternatives.

This lengthy example shows how this method of allowing for escalation can increase the number of calculations. It is bad enough when only periodic costs are involved, as in the example, but when annual expenses have to be considered a cash flow schedule has to be set up. The schedule needs to show the escalated annual cost each year, and then each must be discounted back to present values in a manner similar to that described in the last chapter when taxes were included in the calculation for the internal rate of return. Using the formula or simply deducting the escalation rate from the discount rate greatly simplifies the calculations. The life-cycle costs in this example would then be calculated in the same manner as in Example 1 except that the modified rate would be substituted for the actual discount rate as follows:

$$\text{Modified Rate} = \left(\frac{1 + i}{1 + e} - 1 \right) \times 100$$

$$= \left(\frac{1.10}{1.05} - 1 \right) \times 100$$

$$= 4.76\%$$

	Roof A	Roof B
Initial Cost	$2,000	$3,500
Repair at the end of 10 years:		
$200 x V, 10 years @ 4.76% = $200 x 0.62801 =	126	–
Replacement at the end of 20 years:		
$2,000 x V, 20 years @ 4.76% = $2,000 x 0.39440 =	789	–
Repair at the end of 20 years:		
$200 x V, 20 years @ 4.76% = $200 x 0.39440	–	79
Repair at the end of 30 years:		
$200 x V, 30 years @ 4.76% = $200 x 0.24768 =	50	–
Total present cost	$2,965	$3,579

With a modified rate of 4.76% this method is best done with a financial calculator or a computer.

COSTS

Because life-cycle costing can be used to help members of the design team and the building owner to make rational decisions over a wide range of variables, from a choice between two or more building materials to a choice between two or more overall building designs, the amount of available cost information must be equally wide. Although the cost information usually has to be based on historical data, decisions can only be made about present and future expenditures and the values they can create. Once money has been spent and the building has been constructed, all the decisions have been made and they cannot be recalled.

The costs required for life-cycle costing can be broken down into a number of categories which, because of their application, come under three major headings: capital costs, annual costs, and periodic or cyclical costs.

CAPITAL COSTS

Capital costs are the easiest to estimate. The information is usually readily available and comparisons between materials, systems or buildings on the basis of capital costs are frequently made and well understood. However, costs not directly related to construction may sometimes be required, such as the cost of land when a comparison is being made between the costs of a high-rise structure and a low-rise structure which would require additional land. If construction management is under consideration the effect of the reduction in design and construction time, and any resulting difference in construction cost and design fees, would be assessed and then compared with the value to the building owner of obtaining earlier occupancy.

ANNUAL COSTS

In a financial feasibility study the annual costs are usually considered together under a heading of "Operating Costs" as was done in Chapter 7, but for the purpose of life-cycle costing it is often necessary to separate them as follows:

1. MAINTENANCE COSTS

These are usually defined as those costs which are required in order to maintain the building as far as possible in its original condition. They would include the cost of labour and supplies for daily cleaning, or the cost of a maintenance contract if it is to be done by an outside organization. Also included would be a service contract for the servicing of elevators or other equipment, and minor repairs and upkeep to the building fabric such as the replacement of electric light bulbs or tubes.

Maintenance costs will depend to a large extent on the type of building, public buildings being likely to have higher maintenance costs than buildings in the private sector. They will also depend on the maintenance policy of the building owner. Some owners have a policy of planned maintenance in which maintenance tasks are carried out according to a set schedule. Others rely only on remedial maintenance which, apart from routine cleaning, requires that maintenance work be done only when a failure indicates that it is required. Planned maintenance can result in better use of maintenance staff, less disturbance to the building occupants as maintenance operations can be more conveniently scheduled, a reduction in the need for stand-by equipment because there is less chance of failure in the main equipment, and a more reliable service from the building. On the other hand, planned maintenance is likely to be more costly than remedial maintenance since there will be a greater amount of routine servicing and more frequent replacement of minor components, sometimes before they have reached the end of their lives. However, planned maintenance can also mean that less expensive equipment might be considered for the building because it will be well maintained. An owner who will be relying on remedial maintenance should certainly consider more expensive equipment which is less subject to breakdown.

Estimating the cost of maintenance should be easier when the building owner will be adopting a policy of planned maintenance, but even a building owner with a policy of planned maintenance will tend to spend less on maintenance when there is a downturn in the economy.

Most owners of existing buildings have records of their maintenance costs, although these are generally compiled for accounting purposes and may not be in a form which can provide immediate data for a life-cycle cost study. Even so, the costs which are available can give some indication of the magnitude of maintenance costs for specific buildings, and further analysis can break the costs down into a more suitable form, particularly if they can be discussed with the owner or the building manager. If possible the analysis should go further than revealing the maintenance costs of individual materials and equipment. Ideally they should show the man-hours required for various maintenance operations together with the supplies and equipment required, much as is done when recording data for construction estimating, allowing costs to be readily updated when necessary. A building manager who has already been appointed for a new building when the life-cycle cost studies are being prepared can provide valuable information on the probable maintenance and other anticipated costs, and suggest how these costs may be reduced.

2. OPERATING COSTS

These are costs which are directly related to the operation of the building, such as the cost of fuel, electric power, water, security personnel and the like. They are usually easier to estimate than maintenance costs although some uncertainty can exist in predicting future costs, as was demonstrated some years ago when the cost of fuels for heating systems rose far higher than anyone could have predicted. As has already been mentioned, if there is a possibility that there might be a variation in the difference between operating costs, such as the cost of one fuel increasing at a higher rate than another, this should be allowed for in the life-cycle cost study. However, allowing for escalation in operating costs is only likely to change the ranking between alternatives if the operating costs are large in relation to the capital cost, if the difference between operating costs is likely to increase substantially, or if the difference is likely to take place in the near future.

3. USER COSTS

These are costs relating to the users of a building, such as the cost involved in production in a manufacturing plant, or the cost of medical staff, equipment and supplies in a hospital. Life-cycle cost studies which include user costs are usually concerned with alternative planning solutions to see which provides the most efficient working environment within the building, or with comparisons between the cost of purchasing equipment and the saving in staff which might result from its use. User costs are therefore customarily only required for owner-operated buildings and the costs are not usually difficult to obtain.

4. OTHER ANNUAL COSTS

These might include the cost of financing when considering whether to delay construction until an anticipated reduction in mortgage interest rates takes place. Another example might be the cost of insurance when a decision is needed on the comparative costs of two types of construction, one of which will provide a better fire insurance rating. Although income is not usually thought of as an expense, and is not normally included in life-cycle costs, there may be occasions when the choice between two materials or systems will have an effect on the income potential of a building, in which case the difference in income would have to be included.

Annual costs can represent a major proportion of the total costs of a building over its life, very often equalling if not exceeding the capital cost. The ratio between capital and annual costs will also vary between building types, and within building types it will vary from building to building depending upon how well they have been designed and built, and how well they are managed.

PERIODIC COSTS

Periodic costs would include the following:

1. REPLACEMENT COSTS

These are the costs of replacing those parts of the building such as finishes and equipment which have lives which are shorter than that of the building. Redecorating can be considered as a replacement cost since it is normally a periodic cost and, in effect, it replaces the original decorations. Replacement costs of equipment will apply both to the equipment itself and to its component parts. When making a decision in the design stage between the selection of one piece of equipment which has a high capital cost and a long life, and another which has a lower capital cost but a shorter anticipated life, the decision can depend on more than just the estimated cost of replacement. It may also depend on considerations such as:

1. The anticipated life of the building and whether, in fact, the equipment with the lower capital cost may last as long as the building.
2. The possibility that changes may take place in the function of the building which could make it necessary to replace the equipment in a comparatively short time anyway.
3. The possibility that technological improvements will make the equipment obsolete before it reaches the end of its physical life.

These considerations could make the choice of the less expensive equipment the better decision.

A decision on the cost of replacing a defective component part is more likely to be needed during the life of a building than it is at the design stage of a new building. The available choices might be to replace the component with an identical part; to replace it with an improved model which may be more expensive in capital cost but which is either more efficient, has a greater life expectancy, has lower running costs, or is a combination of all three; or just to repair the defective part. A life-cycle cost study can help reach a decision on the best choice.

The most common materials which have to be replaced during a building's life are roof finishes and interior finishes, particularly floor finishes, although there can be many others including windows, doors, parapet walls, railings and built-in fittings and fixtures. When considering the replacement cost of materials such as floor finishes, the cost of disturbance, if any, to the occupants of the building while replacement is taking place should also be included. As with components, a decision may be needed whether to replace or repair.

2. REPAIRS

These are the costs of repairing those parts of the building which become defective. Repointing brick walls or recaulking windows and doors are periodic expenditures which are fairly predictable and which can be considered as repairs. The type and frequency of other repairs, however, can be very difficult to forecast, although their cost may not necessarily be difficult to estimate. As with most other expenses incurred during the life of a building, so much depends on the way the building is used and maintained, but in the case of repairs it can also depend on the way the building is designed and constructed. Poor detailing, bad workmanship or faulty materials are hardly likely to be expected when a life-cycle cost study is being made but they can result in repairs having to be made much sooner than was anticipated.

Repairs are required when there has been a failure. There have been occasions in the past for the capital cost of the building to be increased in an attempt to avoid a failure which had only a minimal chance of occurring, or which would have been less expensive to repair. A life-cycle cost study would have prevented this unnecessary extra expense.

3. ALTERATION COSTS

Alterations to an existing building are not usually initiated unless there is an evident economic gain to be made, either in making the operations within the building more efficient or in reducing its running costs. Sometimes outside factors can influence the decision, as for example when a change takes place in government policy with respect to the operation of a hospital, or changes in population trends affect the need for schools.

Alteration work is always more expensive than work done at the time a new building is being constructed. This is because it usually has to include the cost of removing existing work before the new work can be constructed, adjacent areas have to be protected and any damage made good, the work is usually on a smaller scale than was the new construction, and working in restricted spaces can add to the cost of labour, both directly at the location of the work and in manhandling materials. Besides these more obvious direct costs there are the costs of disturbance, including the temporary loss of space in the building, the reduction in efficiency in other areas of the building as the activities of the building's occupants have to be rescheduled and furniture and equipment has to be moved, and the noise and dust which is generated while the work is in progress. In some instances these associated costs can be more than the actual cost of construction, involving a loss of production or the need for overtime in a manufacturing plant; the loss of income in a rental building, together with the cost of providing temporary alternative accommodation elsewhere if necessary; and the loss of amenities in a hospital or school. Evaluating these costs may pose some problems, but nevertheless they should be measured and allowed for in a life-cycle cost study.

Because of the cost of alteration work, and the difficulty of predicting when and to what extent it may be required, provision is sometimes made when the building is being constructed to make it more amenable to future alterations. A simple example of this is the use of movable partitions in place of solid partitions. Another example is providing increased structural requirements to give more flexibility for future alterations. It is extremely expensive, supposing it is possible, to make structural alterations in an existing building, and increased column spacing, greater floor-bearing capacity, over-sized foundations and increased storey heights can be incorporated at much less expense at the time of construction than if they have to be provided later.

The inclusion of interstitial space in hospitals has also been used in the past as a means of reducing future alteration costs. It provides additional space separated from the working floors for material handling equipment and the electrical and mechanical services which, in theory, can be altered without disturbing the occupants of the building, and was usually combined with a structural system incorporating long spans which gives greater flexibility to the working floors.

Making structural provisions for future alterations will inevitably add to the capital cost. The structural costs themselves will increase as will the quantity and cost of exterior cladding, partitions and stairs if increased storey heights are required. In addition, the operating costs of the building will be higher if there is a larger building volume to be heated and cooled, and the addition of interstitial space would require extra lighting.

It is difficult to justify making a large increase in capital expenditure to save future costs which may never be incurred, or which may be incurred to a lesser extent than warrants the increase. A life-cycle cost study can help show whether or not it is warranted. It might take the form of estimating the premium in capital costs for providing the additional requirements and discounting this sum over the life of the building to give an annual equivalent. Any additional operating costs would then be added to show a total annual cost and the decision would be based on whether the annual saving in future alteration costs is likely to be more or less than this amount. For example, a premium of $2,000,000 in capital cost for providing interstitial space has an annual equivalent cost of $167,700 over a forty-year period at a discount rate of eight per cent. If the expected premium in operating costs due to the interstitial space is $8,000 a year, the total annual cost will be $175,700.

If the extra cost of making alterations each year in a building without interstitial space can be expected to exceed this amount, then the interstitial space is justified.

Alternatively the study might take the form of finding the period of time within which the capital cost of making provision for future requirements equals the cost of making alterations in the future. The further in the future that alterations are likely to be needed, the less advantage there is in making provision for them at the time of construction. The following example illustrates this method:

Example 10: The owner of a factory which is currently being designed believes that changes in production techniques may require certain alterations to the building at some time in the future. Making provision for these future requirements now will cost an additional $75,000, while making the alterations in the future is estimated to cost $130,000 at current prices. When will the break-even point be, assuming a discount rate of 9% and a construction escalation rate of 5%?

Answer: The modified discount rate incorporating escalation will be 9% less 5%, or 4%. The costs will break even when the capital cost and the present value of the future cost equal each other, that is when:

$$\$130,000 \times V = \$75,000, \text{ or}$$

$$V = \frac{75,000}{130,000}$$

$$= 0.57692$$

Reference to Present Worth of One Dollar tables shows that at a discount rate of 4% this occurs in about fourteen years. If the owner thinks the alterations will be required within the next fourteen years the increased capital expenditure is justified.

This calculation becomes a little more complicated if more than one future expenditure is involved.

Example 11: What will be the break-even point in Example 10 if, in making provision for future requirements the operating costs increase by $1,000 a year?

Answer: The break-even point will be when:

$$\$130,000 \times V = \$75,000 + \$1,000 \times YP, \text{ or}$$

$$\frac{\$130,000 \times V}{\$75,000 + (\$1,000 \times YP)} = 1$$

As with the calculation of the internal rate of return in Chapter 10, this can be solved by interpolation using two target break-even points, in this case 10 and 15 years.

At 10 years:

$$\frac{\$130,000 \times 0.67556}{\$75,000 + (\$1,000 \times 8.11090)}$$

$$= \frac{87,823}{83,111}$$

$$= 1.05670$$

At 15 years:

$$\frac{\$130,000 \times 0.55526}{\$75,000 + (\$1,000 \times 11.11839)}$$

$$= \frac{72,184}{86,118}$$

$$= 0.83820$$

Break-even point:

$$\text{Lower life} + \frac{HR - 1.0}{HR - LR} \ (\text{Higher life} - \text{Lower life})$$

$$= 10 + \frac{1.0567 - 1.0}{1.0567 - 0.8382} \times (15 - 10)$$

$$= 10 + \frac{0.0567}{0.2185} \times 5$$

$$= 10 + 1.29748$$

$$= 11.29748 \text{ years}$$

With the additional operating costs the increased capital expenditure is now justified only if the owner thinks the alterations will be required within a little over eleven years.

In practice it is hardly necessary to go into the amount of detail shown in this example. A glance at the ratio produced for ten years shows that the break-even point won't be much beyond ten years because it is close to 1.0, and this is probably near enough.

Another aspect of alteration costs is that of having to decide whether to renovate an existing building, or whether to demolish and rebuild. Money spent on renovating existing buildings – which may only have a limited life anyway – is not then available for constructing new buildings, and despite the renovations an existing building may lack the amenities of a new one and have higher maintenance and operating costs. A life-cycle cost study in this instance could take the form of a feasibility study showing the present value of the renovated building for comparison with the present value of a new building. Although this will help make an economic decision about whether or not to renovate, the decision sometimes is not entirely an economic one. It may be influenced by such things as community interests and pressures, architectural merit, or other intangible factors.

4. SALVAGE

This, like income, can be considered a negative cost. Some materials and equipment may have a salvage value at the end of their life and this should be included in a life-cycle cost study when appropriate. Salvage will also help offset the cost of demolition. Although demolition is generally thought of as being the cost of demolishing an existing building prior to the erection of a new one, and would therefore be a capital cost rather than a periodic cost, there will be occasions when demolition and salvage can be considered as periodic costs occurring once at the end of a building's life.

5. OTHER COSTS

The capital, annual and periodic costs just described cover most of the tangible costs which might be needed for life-cycle costing. There are, however, other costs which might be needed and which are much harder to estimate. These might relate to the appearance of the building, to the standards of comfort and safety of those working in it, and to the effect of the building on the surrounding community. Appearance has already been mentioned as a factor which will depend on the building owner's objectives and assessing any difference in potential income because of the building's appearance should not be difficult. However assessing the ease of raising capital or the advertising value which will accrue to a building of enhanced prestige is more problematical. Improving the standards of comfort and safety for the building's occupants might be reflected in improved staff morale and could be related to a possible reduction in staff turnover. The effect of the building on the community is rarely considered by most building owners unless it reflects directly on the profitability of the building or the business which is being carried on within it. Such things as improved access and parking, superior landscaping, and noise abatement and anti-pollution devices beyond those required by the law might all be considered as reflecting a building owner's regard for the community but, while estimating their costs may not be difficult, placing a value on them is something only the building owner can do.

TAXATION

Taxation is not a factor which needs to be considered in life-cycle cost studies for public buildings such as government offices, hospitals and schools. Whether it needs to be considered in a study for a private owner depends on the objectives of the study. From the last chapter, which showed how taxation might be incorporated into the financial feasibility study of a development project, it can be seen that the amount of tax building owners pay on their developments depends not only on current tax regulations but also on their own fiscal policies, combined with their method of financing and the income potential of their building. For this reason the taxes they have to pay can fluctuate widely, making it difficult to incorporate them into a study and, unless they can be seen to have a direct bearing on a comparison between the costs of individual materials, components or systems, taxes can usually be excluded from a life-cycle cost study.

Taxes will, however, have a direct bearing where large capital expenditures and operating costs are involved, such as a study on the selection of major pieces of equipment or a comparison between alternative building designs. Because taxes on capital expenditures are calculated on a diminishing balance over the life of the building whereas operating costs are treated as a current expense for tax purposes, the inclusion of taxes for each type of expenditure could make a difference to the outcome in this type of study and taxation would need to be taken into account.

ERROR ANALYSIS

Life-cycle costing involves attempting to forecast the future, usually well into the future, and it must be based on numerous assumptions. Assumptions can sometimes prove to be wrong, so it is advisable to be able to test them to see whether any variations will affect the validity of the results.

Assumptions have to be made about both capital and future costs. It might be considered that any error in costs could be self-cancelling because life-cycle costing is concerned with comparative costs, not with absolute costs. While this is true in some circumstances and complete accuracy in the cost is not usually considered essential, there can obviously be occasions when an error in the costs can affect the ranking. If the costs being compared both err in the same direction, that is they have both been overestimated or underestimated, or if the higher cost has been underestimated, or the lower cost has been overestimated, there will be no change in the ranking. However, if the costs being compared err in opposite directions, or the higher cost has been overestimated, or the lower cost has been underestimated, the ranking can be changed. If, for example, two wall assemblies are being compared, one with a capital cost of $100,000 and the other with a cost of $110,000, a change in ranking can take place in the following circumstances:

(a) The higher cost has been overestimated and the lower cost has been underestimated by about five per cent: $110,000 - 5% = $104,500
$100,000 + 5% = $105,000

(b) The higher cost has been overestimated by a little over nine per cent:
$110,000 - 9.09% = $100,001

(c) The lower cost has been underestimated by ten per cent:
$100,000 + 10% = $110,000

If it is considered unlikely that errors will exceed these percentages, the capital costs of the two wall assemblies can be considered to be acceptable and unlikely to produce errors in their life-cycle costs. The possibility of changes in future costs can be assessed in a similar manner. If two heating systems have estimated operating costs, one of $12,500 and the other of $9,500 per year, the more expensive system would have to reduce its operating costs by twenty-four per cent to make it comparable with the less expensive system, and the probability of this happening would have to be judged in making a decision.

The effects of changes in the discount rate and in the assumed life of the building have already been mentioned. The extent to which these will affect the ranking in life-cycle cost studies will depend to a large degree on the ratio between the capital costs and future costs, particularly annual costs, and special care is needed when one design has a low capital cost and high annual costs while the alternative has the reverse. It is often worthwhile carrying out sensitivity analysis to see what effect changes in the costs, the discount rate and the assumed life of the building or the materials or components will have on the results.

Example 12: What will be the effect on the comparison made in Example 3 if Floor A needs replacing only every fifteen years and the discount rate is increased to ten per cent?

Answer:	Floor A	Floor B
Initial cost	$10,000	$15,000
Replacement costs:		
V @ 10%, 15 years = 0.23939		
30 years = 0.05731		
0.29670		
Floor A: $10,000 x 0.29670 =	2,967	–
Floor B: $15,000 x 0.29670 =	–	4,451
Maintenance:		
Floor A: $1,200 x YP, 40 years @ 10%		
= $1,200 x 9.77905 =	11,735	–
Floor B: $800 x YP, 40 years @ 10%		
= $800 x 9.77905 =	–	7,823
Total present cost	$24,702	$27,274

These changes to the expected life of Floor A and the discount rate have reversed the order found in Example 3, and Floor A is now the less expensive.

This example shows how changes in two of the assumptions can affect the ranking of the alternatives. The number of changes which could be tested is limitless so it is advisable to restrict them only to those assumptions which are felt to be subject to variation. Generally speaking, the testing should be restricted to the outer limits of the possible variations, unless a computer is available, in which case a wide range of variations in discount rates, lives, costs and escalation rates can be tested and, if necessary, plotted on graphs to demonstrate visually how they affect the ranking of the alternatives.

CONCLUSION

It has been suggested that a building owner who expects to sell the building after a few years would have no need for life-cycle cost studies since the new owner would be responsible for its maintenance and operating costs. A similar argument has been made for publicly owned buildings since one government department is responsible for the capital costs and another for the maintenance and operating costs. However, since the objective of a life-cycle cost study is to help give the building owner value for money, the outcome should be an increase in the value of the building. For the private owner this could be reflected in the price the new owner is prepared to pay for the building, so both the original and the new owner will reap the benefits of the study. In the case of the public owner, public money should be spent wisely regardless of which department is spending it.

Care needs to be taken when making decisions based on life-cycle cost studies and a proper balance must be struck. Too much emphasis on making capital expenditures to save future costs can result in a financial burden which can inhibit a building owner's future actions almost as much as spending too little on capital costs and having high maintenance and operating costs.

All the previous examples in this chapter have given comparatively simple illustrations of the way in which life-cycle cost studies might be performed. The next, and final, example gives a more complex illustration incorporating many of the factors which have been discussed.

Example 13: Which of the following two exterior walls is the more economical given the following data all of which relates directly to the exterior walls:

	Wall Type A	Wall Type B
Initial cost of the wall, per m²	$155.00	$160.00
Total area of the wall, m²	12,300	12,300
Salvage value, per m² of wall	$8.00	$18.00
Cleaning exterior, per m² of wall:		
Every 25 years	$11.85	–
Every 6 months	–	$2.80
Caulking exterior, per m² of wall:		
Every 10 years	–	$7.50
Painting interior, per m² of wall:		
Every 4 years	$5.50	–
Fire insurance, per $100 building cost:		
Building, per annum	$0.08	$0.10
Contents, per annum	$0.20	$0.25
Hydro costs, per annum	$90,200	$85,400

Fuel and maintenance costs per annum	$60,300	$65,000
Rental rate, per m²	$225.00	$225.00
Total gross floor area of the building, m²	25,600	25,600
Cost per m² gross for the building	$1,020.00	$1,034.00
Total capital cost of the foundations	$1,520,000	$1,460,000
Total capital cost of electrical	$4,360,000	$4,240,000
Total capital cost of heating and air conditioning	$5,630,000	$5,740,000
Total net floor area of the building, m²	19,340	19,650

Assume the life of the building to be 40 years, and the discount rate to be 9%.

Answer:

Wall Type A

Initial cost of wall: 12,300m² @ $155.00 =	$1,906,500
Premium for foundations: $1,520,000 - $1,460,000 =	60,000
Premium for electrical: $4,360,000 - $4,240,000 =	120,000

Premium for hydro costs: ($90,200 - $85,400) x YP, 40 years @ 9%

= $4,800 x 10.75736 =	51,635

Cleaning exterior: 12,300m² @ $11.48 = $145,755

$145,755 x V, 25 years @ 9% = $145,755 x 0.11597 =	16,903

Painting interior: 12,300m² x $5.50 = $67,650

V @ 9% for		
4 years	= 0.70843
8 years	= 0.50187
12 years	= 0.35553
16 years	= 0.25187
20 years	= 0.17843
24 years	= 0.12640
28 years	= 0.08955
32 years	= 0.06344
36 years	= 0.04494
	————
	2.32046
	========

$67,650 x V = $67,650 x 2.32046 =	156,979
	————
	$2,312,017

Less Salvage value: 12,300m² @ $8.00 = $98,400

$98,400 x V, 40 years @ 9% = $98,400 x 0.03184 =	(3,133)
	————
Total present cost of Wall Type A	$2,308,884
	========

Wall Type B
Initial cost of wall: 12,300m² @ $160.00 = $1,968,000

Premium for heating and air conditioning:
  $5,740,000 - $5,630,000 =   110,000

Premium for design fees: 6% of $358,400 =   21,504

Premium for fire insurance:
  Type B -   Building cost: 25,600m² @ $1,034.00
             = $26,470,400
             Annual premium = 264,704 @ $0.35 = $92,646
  Type A -   Building cost: 25,600m² @ $1,020.00
             = $26,112,000
             Annual premium = 261,120 @ $0.28 = $73,114
                                                            _____
             Additional premium $19,532
                                                            ========
        $19,532 x YP, 40 years @ 9% = $19,532 x 10.75736 =   210,113

Cleaning exterior: $2.80 every 6 months = $5.60 per year
        12,300m² @ $5.60 = $68,880
        $68,880 x YP, 40 years @ 9% = $68,880 x 10.75736 =   740,967

Premium for fuel and maintenance costs: $65,000 - $60,300
        = $4,700 x YP, 40 years @ 9% = $4,700 x 10.75736 =   50,560

Caulking exterior: 12,300m² x $7.50 = $92,250
        V @ 9% for 10 years   = 0.42241
                    20 years   = 0.17843
                    30 years   = 0.07537
                                   _____
                                   0.67621
                                   ========
        $92,250 x V = $92,250 x 0.67621 =   62,380
                                                                               _____
                                                                              $3,163,414

  Less   Increased income: 19,650m² - 19,340m²
         = 310 m² @ $225.00 = $69,750
         $69,750 x YP, 40 years @ 9% = $69,750 x 10.75736 =   (750,326)

  Less   Salvage value: 12,300m² @ $18.00 = $221,400
         $221,400 x V, 40 years @ 9% = $221,400 x 0.03184 =   (7,049)
                                                                               _____
         Total present cost of Wall Type B $2,406,039
                                                                               ========

WALL A is the more economical, both in capital and in life-cycle costs.

The credit for increased income shown for WALL B is due to the difference in thickness of the two walls, giving the building with WALL B a greater net floor area than with WALL A.

Life-cycle costing is appropriate in a variety of situations when a building is being designed or renovated, or when replacements or repairs are being considered and is applicable whenever capital costs, running costs and lives of alternatives differ.

APPENDIX A

OUTLINE SPECIFICATION

PROJECT _____

LOCATION _____

JOB NO. _____

BUILDING TYPE _____

ARCHITECT _____

    Representative _____   Tel. No. _____

    Architect's Job No. _____

STRUCTURAL ENGINEER _____

    Representative _____   Tel. No. _____

MECHANICAL ENGINEER _____

    Representative _____   Tel. No. _____

ELECTRICAL ENGINEER _____

    Representative _____   Tel. No. _____

OTHER CONSULTANT_____

    Representative _____   Tel. No. _____

ESTIMATE NO. _____   DATE _____

Please return to:

1.

This document is intended to be used as a checklist for a pre-tender estimate or as an outline specification to accompany a detailed cost analysis. When used as a checklist it is recognized that it will not always be possible to complete it fully but as much information as is available should be entered, and where assumptions have been made they should be so noted.

GENERAL INFORMATION

ESTIMATING SCHEDULE - This estimate due: _____

Anticipated Tender Date: _____

ANTICIPATED LENGTH OF CONSTRUCTION: _____ Months

TYPE OF CONTRACT: _____

SALES TAX: To be included [ ]   Exempt [ ]

A1 SUBSTRUCTURE

  A11 FOUNDATIONS

    Soil Conditions: _____

    Type of Foundation: _____

    Disposal of Excavated Material: _____

    Type of Backfill: _____

    Foundation Walls: _____

    Concrete Strength - Wall Footings: _____

                   Column Footings: _____

                   Walls: _____

                   Columns: _____

    Weeping Tile: _____

    Special Conditions - Rock Excavation: _____

                   Water Conditions: _____

                   Piles: _____

                   Caissons: _____

                   Underpinning: _____

    Comments: _____

    _____

2.

A12 BASEMENT EXCAVATION

Average Depth Below Existing Ground Level: _____

Type of Backfill: _____

Sheet Piling: _____

Comments: _____

_____

A2 STRUCTURE

A21 LOWEST FLOOR CONSTRUCTION

Type of Slab: _____

Concrete Slab -   Thickness: _____   Concrete Strength: _____

Fill Under Slab: _____

Vapour Barrier: _____

Waterproofing: _____

Skim Coat -   Thickness: _____   Concrete Strength: _____

Reinforcing -   Type: _____   Mass: _____ kg per m^2

Comments: _____

_____

A22 UPPER FLOOR CONSTRUCTION

Type of Construction: _____

_____

Bay Size or Span: _____

Superimposed Load: _____

Slab Thicknesses: _____

Column Sizes: _____

Concrete Strengths -   Slabs and Beams: _____

                         Columns: _____

Steel Framing -   Structural Steel: _____ kg per m^2

                    Steel Joists: _____ kg per m^2

Reinforcing Steel -   Beams and Slabs only: _____ kg per m^2

                        Columns only: _____ kg per m^2

                        Beams, Slabs and Columns: _____ kg per m^2

3.

A22 UPPER FLOOR CONSTRUCTION (CONTINUED)

Metal Deck: _____

Fireproofing -   Slabs: _____

                        Beams: _____

                        Columns: _____

Catwalks: _____

Stairs: _____

Comments: _____

_____

A23 ROOF CONSTRUCTION

Type of Construction: _____

_____

Bay Size or Span: _____

Superimposed Load: _____

Slab Thicknesses: _____

Column Sizes: _____

Concrete Strengths -   Slabs and Beams: _____

                              Columns: _____

Steel Framing -   Structural Steel: _____ kg per m^2

                        Steel Joists: _____ kg per m^2

Reinforcing Steel -   Beams and Slabs only: _____ kg per m^2

                           Columns only: _____ kg per m^2

                           Beams, Slabs and Columns: _____ kg per m^2

Metal Deck: _____

Fireproofing -   Slabs: _____

                        Beams: _____

                        Columns: _____

Comments: _____

_____

4.

A3 EXTERIOR ENCLOSURE

A31 WALLS BELOW GRADE

Type of Wall: _____

Thickness: _____

Concrete Strength: _____

Reinforcing: _____

Waterproofing: _____

Dampproofing: _____

Comments: _____

_____

A32 WALLS ABOVE GRADE

Type of Wall: _____

Thickness: _____

Facing or Exterior Finish: _____

Back-up: _____

Insulation: _____

Vapour Barrier: _____

Comments: _____

_____

A33 WINDOWS & ENTRANCES

Windows -   Type: _____   Material: _____

Finish: _____   Glass: _____

Louvres: _____

Exterior Screens -   Type: _____   Material: _____

Finish: _____   Glass: _____

Doors: _____

Exterior Doors: _____

Hardware: _____

Comments: _____

_____

5.

A34 ROOF COVERING

Type of Roof: _____

Material: _____

Insulation: _____

Vapour Barrier: _____

Flashings: _____

Skylights: _____

Roof Domes: _____

Roof Hatches: _____

Eaves Soffits: _____

Comments: _____

_____

A35 PROJECTIONS

Roof Projections: _____

Floor Projections: _____

Balconies: _____

Canopies: _____

Parapet Walls: Materials _____

Height: _____

Areaways: _____

Chimneys: _____

Comments: _____

_____

General Comments on SHELL:

_____

_____

_____

_____

_____

_____

_____

_____

6.

B1 PARTITIONS & DOORS

B11 PARTITIONS

Block: _____

Thickness: _____

Concrete: _____

Thickness: _____ Strength: _____

Reinforcing: _____

Metal Stud and Drywall: _____

Demountable: _____

Movable: _____

Operable: _____

Glazed Screens: _____

Railings and Balustrades: _____

Comments: _____

_____

B12 DOORS

Wood: _____

Finish: _____ Hardware: _____

Hollow Metal: _____

Finish: _____ Hardware: _____

Glazed Doors: _____

Finish: _____ Hardware: _____

Glass: _____

Fire Doors: _____

Finish: _____ Hardware: _____

Special Doors: _____

Finish: _____ Hardware: _____

Hatches or Access Doors: _____

Frames: _____

Comments: _____

_____

7.

B2 FINISHES

B21 FLOOR FINISHES

Floors				Base		
Concrete -	Steel Trowel	_____	%	Cement	_____	%
	Hardener	_____	%	Rubber	_____	%
	Painted	_____	%	Vinyl	_____	%
Vinyl Composition Tile		_____	%	Carpet	_____	%
High Content Vinyl Tile		_____	%	Quarry Tile	_____	%
Sheet Vinyl		_____	%	Ceramic Tile	_____	%
Rubber Tile		_____	%	Terrazzo	_____	%
Sheet Rubber		_____	%	Stone	_____	%
Carpet		_____	%	Slate	_____	%
Wood		_____	%	Marble	_____	%
Parquet		_____	%	Wood	_____	%
Quarry Tile		_____	%	Metal	_____	%
Ceramic Tile		_____	%	_____	_____	%
Terrazzo		_____	%			
Epoxy		_____	%			
Stone Paving		_____	%			
Slate Paving		_____	%			
Brick Paving		_____	%			
Marble		_____	%			
_____		_____	%			
		100 %		**100 %**		

Topping _____ thick   _____ %

Comments: _____

_____

_____

_____

_____

8.

B22 CEILING FINISHES

Exposed Structure	_____ % of which	_____ % painted
Painted Wallboard	_____ % of which	_____ % suspended
Painted Plaster	_____ % of which	_____ % suspended
Acoustic Tile	_____ % of which	_____ % suspended
Metal Strip	_____ %		
Wood	_____ %		
Illuminated	_____ %		
_____	_____ %		
	100 %		

Bulkheads: _____

Cornices: _____

Comments: _____

_____

B23 WALL FINISHES

Exposed Block or Concrete	_____ % of which	_____ % painted
Plaster	_____ % of which	_____ % painted
Acoustic Plaster	_____ % of which	_____ % painted
Paint	_____ %		
Special Coating	_____ %		
Ceramic Tile	_____ %		
Wood Panelling	_____ %		
Brick Facing	_____ %		
Marble Facing	_____ %		
_____	_____ %		
	100 %		

Corner Guards: _____

Dado Rails: _____

Comments: _____

_____

9.

B3 FITTINGS & EQUIPMENT

B31 FITTINGS & FIXTURES

Locate on drawings and identify by number:

(1) Ash Trays ( )	(24) Lockers ( )
(2) Benches ( )	(25) Mail Boxes ( )
(3) Bleachers ( )	(26) Milk Cabinets ( )
(4) Blinds ( )	(27) Mirrors ( )
(5) Bollards ( )	(28) Music Instrument Racks ( )
(6) Bulletin Boards ( )	(29) Nurses' Stations ( )
(7) Carrels ( )	(30) Parking Booths ( )
(8) Chalkboards ( )	(31) Planters ( )
(9) Coat Racks ( )	(32) Projection Screens ( )
(10) Counters ( )	(33) Seats ( )
(11) Cupboards, Wood ( )	(34) Shelving, Wood ( )
(12) Cupboards, Metal ( )	(35) Shelving, Metal ( )
(13) Curtain Track ( )	(36) Shower Compartments ( )
(14) Directory Boards ( )	(37) Shutters and Grilles ( )
(15) Fireplaces ( )	(38) Tackboards ( )
(16) Flagpoles ( )	(39) Telephone Enclosures ( )
(17) Handrails ( )	(40) Toilet Compartments ( )
(18) Information Booths ( )	(41) Turnstiles ( )
(19) Janitors' Shelves ( )	(42) Washroom Accessories ( )
(20) Kitchen Counters ( )	(43) Waste Receptacles ( )
(21) Kitchen Cupboards ( )	(44) _____ ( )
(22) Ladders ( )	(45) _____ ( )
(23) Library Shelving ( )	(46) _____ ( )

Comments: _____

_____

_____

_____

_____

_____

10.

B32 EQUIPMENT

Bowling Alley Equipment	In Contract ( )	NIC ( )
Conveyors	In Contract ( )	NIC ( )
Cranes and Monorails	In Contract ( )	NIC ( )
Cyclorama	In Contract ( )	NIC ( )
Dock Levellers	In Contract ( )	NIC ( )
Dryers	In Contract ( )	NIC ( )
Garbage Disposal	In Contract ( )	NIC ( )
Greenhouse	In Contract ( )	NIC ( )
Gymnasium Equipment	In Contract ( )	NIC ( )
Hospital Equipment	In Contract ( )	NIC ( )
Incinerators	In Contract ( )	NIC ( )
Kitchen Equipment	In Contract ( )	NIC ( )
Laboratory Equipment	In Contract ( )	NIC ( )
Laundry Equipment	In Contract ( )	NIC ( )
Mortuary Refrigerators	In Contract ( )	NIC ( )
Pneumatic Tube System	In Contract ( )	NIC ( )
Projection Room Equipment	In Contract ( )	NIC ( )
Refrigerators	In Contract ( )	NIC ( )
Sauna Equipment	In Contract ( )	NIC ( )
School Shop Equipment	In Contract ( )	NIC ( )
Stoves	In Contract ( )	NIC ( )
Swimming Pool Equipment	In Contract ( )	NIC ( )
Truck Washing Equipment	In Contract ( )	NIC ( )
Vending Machines	In Contract ( )	NIC ( )
Washing Machines	In Contract ( )	NIC ( )
Window Washing	In Contract ( )	NIC ( )
_____	In Contract ( )	NIC ( )
_____	In Contract ( )	NIC ( )
_____	In Contract ( )	NIC ( )

Comments: _____

_____

11.

B33 CONVEYING SYSTEMS

Passenger Elevators -   Capacity: _____   Speed: _____

Type: _____

Freight Elevators -   Capacity: _____   Speed: _____

Type: _____

Dumbwaiters -   Capacity: _____   Speed: _____

Type: _____

Hoists -   Capacity: _____   Speed: _____

Type: _____

Escalators -   Capacity: _____   Width: _____

Type: _____

Moving Walks -   Capacity: _____   Width: _____

Type: _____

Conveyors: _____

Pneumatic Tube System: _____

Turntables: _____

Chutes: _____

Comments: _____

_____

General Comments on INTERIORS:

_____

_____

_____

_____

_____

_____

_____

_____

_____

_____

_____

12.

C SERVICES

See Mechanical & Electrical checklists

D1 SITE WORK

D11 SITE DEVELOPMENT

Area of the Site: _____

Topography: _____

Clearing and Grubbing: _____

Tree Removal: _____

Grading: _____

Soil Stabilization: _____

Site Watering: _____

Embankments: _____

Paving: _____

Line Painting: _____

Curbs: _____

Bumpers: _____

Parking Lines: _____

Steps: _____

Seeding: _____

Sodding: _____

Planters: _____

Planting: _____

Pools: _____

Fountains: _____

Tennis Courts: _____

Running Track: _____

Playground: _____

Playground Equipment: _____

Outside Sports Facilities: _____

Permanent Signs: _____

Retaining Walls: _____

Rails and Barriers: _____

13.

D1 SITE DEVELOPMENT (CONTINUED)

Fences: _____

Site Furnishings: _____

Flagpoles: _____

Canopies and Covered Ways: _____

_____

Miscellaneous Structures: _____

Other Site Work: _____

Landscaping Allowance $_____

Comments: _____

_____

D12 SITE MECHANICAL

See Mechanical checklist

D13 SITE ELECTRICAL

See Electrical checklist

D21 DEMOLITION

Existing Buildings - To Remain   ( )

To be Demolished   ( )

In Contract ( )   N.I.C. ( )

Comments: _____

_____

D22 ALTERATIONS

Alterations to the Existing Building:

In Contract ( )   N.I.C. ( )   None ( )

Comments: _____

_____

General Comments on SITE & ANCILLARY WORK:

_____

_____

_____

14.

Z GENERAL REQUIREMENTS & ALLOWANCES

   Z1 GENERAL REQUIREMENTS & FEE

      Building permit -   By Owner: ( )   By Contractor: ( )

      Bid Bond -   Required: ( )   Not Required: ( )

      Performance Bond - ____%   Required: ( )   Not Required: ( )

      All Risks Insurance -   By Owner: ( )   By Contractor: ( )

      General Requirements: ____%

      Fee: ____%

      Total: ____%

      Comments: _____

   Z2 ALLOWANCES

      Design Allowance   ____%

      Escalation Allowance   ____%

      Construction Allowance   ____%

      Comments: _____

      General Comments on GENERAL REQUIREMENTS & ALLOWANCES

15.

APPENDIX B

This document is intended to be used as a checklist for a pre-tender estimate or as an outline specification to accompany a detailed cost analysis for mechanical and electrical work.

CLARE, RANDALL-SMITH & ASSOCIATES LIMITED

53 LESMILL ROAD, DON MILLS, ONTARIO M3B 2T8   (416) 445 - 8166

OUTLINE SPECIFICATION

PROJECT   _____

PROJECT NO.   _____

DATE   _____

CLIENT   _____

    REPRESENTATIVE   _____ Tel. No._____

LOCATION   _____

BUILDING TYPE   _____

ARCHITECT   _____

    REPRESENTATIVE   _____ Tel. No._____

MECHANICAL ENGINEER   _____

    REPRESENTATIVE   _____ Tel. No._____

ELECTRICAL ENGINEER   _____

    REPRESENTATIVE   _____ Tel. No._____

STRUCTURAL ENGINEER   _____

    REPRESENTATIVE   _____ Tel. No._____

CONSTRUCTION PERIOD   _____

COMMENCEMENT DATE   _____

NUMBER OF FLOORS   _____

GROSS FLOOR AREA   _____

INDOOR PARKING AREA   _____

NO. OF HOSPITAL BEDS   _____

NO. OF HOTEL ROOMS   _____

SEATING CAPACITY   _____

OTHER INFORMATION   _____

                                _____

                                _____

                                _____

MECHANICAL & ELECTRICAL QUANTITY SURVEYORS AND CONSTRUCTION ECONOMISTS

C1   **MECHANICAL**

C11   PLUMBING & DRAINAGE

C111   Equipment

Sewage Pumps _____

Sump Pumps _____

Submersible Pumps _____

Domestic Hot Water Tanks _____

Domestic Hot Water Heaters _____

Domestic Recirc. Pumps _____

Domestic Cold Water
 Booster Pumps _____

Expansion Tanks _____

Pressure Reducing Valves _____

Drainage Products _____

   Floor Drains _____

   Roof Drains _____

   Trap Seals _____

   Outside H.B. _____

Oil Interceptors _____

Grease Interceptors _____

Thermostatic Mixing Valves _____

Water Treatment (Softeners
 etc.) _____

Other _____

_____

C112   Piping

Inside Buried Piping

   Storm _____

   Sanitary _____

   Water _____

   Corrosive Resistant
 Drainage _____

   Sub Soil Drains
 (Weepers) _____

   Fire Lines _____

   Other _____

_____

Above Ground Piping (Standard)

   Rainwater Leaders _____

   Sanitary Waste _____

   Sanitary Vents _____

   Domestic Water _____

   Insulation _____

   Other _____

_____

_____

CLARE, RANDALL-SMITH & ASSOCIATES LIMITED

- 2 -

C1 **MECHANICAL**
C11 PLUMBING & DRAINAGE
C112 Piping (cont'd)
    Above Ground Piping (Special)
        Chilled Drinking Water
        High Temperature Water
         180^0
        Tempered Water 110^0
        CO^2 System
        Medical Oxygen
        Medical Vacuum
        Medical Air
        Nitrous Oxide
        Nitrogen
        De-ionized Water
        Compressed Air
        Distilled Water
        Laboratory Waste & Vent
        Gas Piping
        Kitchen Equipment Piping
        Other

C113 Fixtures
    Regular Fixtures
        W.C. (Tank) (Floor)
         (Wall)
        W.C. (F.V.) (Floor) (Wall)
        W.C. Carrier
        Bidets
        Urinals (Stall) (Wall) (FV)
         (Tank)
        Urinal Carriers
        Lavatories (W.H.)
        Lavatory Carriers
        Lavatories (C.I.)
        Bradley Washfountains
        Baths
        Showers
        Drinking Fountains
        Water Coolers
        Sinks
        Service
        Laundry Tubs
        Washroom Accessories
        Soap Systems
        Barrier Free Requirements
        Electronic Faucets & Flush
         Valves
        Other

CLARE, RANDALL-SMITH & ASSOCIATES LIMITED

C1   **MECHANICAL**
C11   PLUMBING & DRAINAGE
C113   Fixtures (cont'd)
         Hospital Fixtures
           Bed Pan Cleaners   _____
           Baths - Institutional   _____
           Baths - Emergency   _____
           Baths - Arm   _____
           Baths - Sitz   _____
           Baths - Foot   _____
           Baths - Pre-Natal   _____
           Baths - Infants   _____
           Baths - Hydro Therapy   _____
           Therapy Swim Pool   _____
           Sinks - Scrub Up   _____
           Sinks - Plaster & Trap   _____
           Sinks - Flushing Rim   _____
           Sinks - Medicine   _____
           Sinks - Utility   _____
           Emergency Showers   _____
           Emergency Eye Wash   _____
           Flushing Rim Floor Drains   _____
           Laboratory Fitments   _____
           Other   _____
             _____

C114   Special Piping & Fixtures
         Incinerators (Waste)   _____
         Incinerators (Pathological)   _____
         Concrete Work (bases etc.)   _____
         Covers & Frames   _____
         Steel Gratings   _____
         Starters & Wiring   _____
         Painting   _____
         Hoisting   _____

         Vacuum Cleaning Systems   _____
         Pneumatic Tube System   _____
         Kitchen Equipment   _____
         Laundry Equipment   _____
         High Purity Water Systems   _____
         Medical Air Compressors   _____
         Medical Vacuum Pumps   _____
         Oxygen Manifolds   _____
         Nitrogen Manifolds   _____
         Zone Valve Boxes   _____
         Medical Alarm Panels   _____
         Medical Gas Wall Outlets   _____
         Other   _____
           _____

CLARE, RANDALL-SMITH & ASSOCIATES LIMITED

- 4 -

C1   **MECHANICAL**
C12   FIRE PROTECTION
C121   Equipment
      Siamese Connections   _____
      Backflow Preventers   _____
      Fire Booster Pumps   _____
      Jockey Pumps   _____
      Fire Hose Cabinets   _____
      Fire Department Valves   _____
      Fire Hose Racks   _____
      Roof Manifolds   _____
      Fire Extinguishers   _____
      Specialized Fire Suppression   _____
      Other   _____
      _____

C122   Piping & Sprinkler Heads
      Fire Standpipe   _____
      Sprinklers   _____
      Upright Sprinkler Heads   _____
      Pendant Sprinkler Heads   _____
      Side Wall Sprinkler Heads   _____
      Specialized Sprinkler Heads   _____
      Other   _____

C1   HVAC
C131   Equipment
      1. Heat Generation
      Boiler:
         Gas Fired   _____
         Oil Fired   _____
         Electric   _____
         Hot Water   _____
         Steam   _____
         Low Pressure   _____
         High Pressure   _____
         Type   _____
         Horsepower / MBH   _____
      Boiler Circulation Pumps   _____
      Expansion Tanks   _____
      Breeching   _____
      Stacks   _____
      Blow Down Tank   _____
      De-aerator   _____
      Boiler Chemical Treatment   _____
      Water softener for Boilers   _____
      Other   _____

CLARE, RANDALL-SMITH & ASSOCIATES LIMITED

C1　　**MECHANICAL**
C13　　HVAC
C131　　Equipment (cont'd)
　　　　2. Electric Heat
　　　　Baseboard Heaters　_____
　　　　Wall Heaters　_____
　　　　Unit Heaters　_____

　　　　3. Refrigeration
　　　　Centrifugal Chiller　_____
　　　　Heat Recovery Chiller　_____
　　　　Water Cooled Chiller　_____
　　　　Air Cooled Chiller　_____
　　　　Condensers　_____
　　　　Condensing Units　_____
　　　　Cooling Towers - Draw-Thru　_____
　　　　Cooling Towers - Induced
　　　　 Draft　_____
　　　　Cooling Towers - Closed
　　　　 Circuit　_____
　　　　Expansion Tanks　_____
　　　　Chilled Water Pumps　_____
　　　　Condenser Water Pumps　_____
　　　　Plate Type Heat Exchangers　_____
　　　　Variable Speed Drives　_____
　　　　Ice Storage Tanks　_____
　　　　Water Treatment　_____

　　　　4. Liquid Heat Transfer (Heating)
　　　　Steam to Steam Heat
　　　　 Exchangers　_____
　　　　Steam to Water Heat
　　　　 Exchangers　_____
　　　　Hot Water Generators　_____
　　　　Primary Heating Pumps　_____
　　　　Secondary Heating Pumps　_____
　　　　Coil Circulating Pumps　_____

　　　　5. Steam & Condensate
　　　　Steam PRV Stations　_____
　　　　Condensate Pumps - Simplex　_____
　　　　Condensate Pumps - Duplex　_____
　　　　Steam Humidifiers　_____
　　　　　_____
　　　　　_____
　　　　　_____

CLARE, RANDALL-SMITH & ASSOCIATES LIMITED

C1   **MECHANICAL**
C13   HVAC
C131   Equipment (cont'd)
6. Liquid Heat Transfer (Cooling)
Circulating Pumps   _____
Coil Circulating Pumps   _____
Fan Coil Units   _____
Heat Pumps   _____
Computer Room A/C Units _____
Thru-wall A/C Units   _____
Window A/C Units   _____

7. Energy Recovery
Air to Air Heat Exchanger _____
Heat Recovery Wheel   _____
Glycol Coils   _____
Glycol Pumps   _____

8. Air Handling Equipment
Packaged Air Handling Units
Pre-Engineered Air Handling
 Units   _____
Custom Built Air Handling
 Units
Roof Top Air Handling Units _____

Check List for Air Handling Units:
   Heating Coil   _____
   Cooling Coil   _____
   DX Cooling Coil   _____
   Glycol Heating Coil _____
   Steam Heating Coil _____
   Electric Heat   _____
   Gas Fired   _____
   Constant Volume   _____
   Variable Volume   _____
   Variable Inlet Vanes _____
   Variable Speed Drives _____
   Multi-Zone   _____
   Type of Filters   _____
   Single or Double Wall
    Construction   _____
   Economizers   _____
   Return Air Fan   _____
   Humidification   _____
   Air Blenders   _____

CLARE, RANDALL-SMITH & ASSOCIATES LIMITED

- 7 -

C1	**MECHANICAL**	
C13	HVAC	
C131	Equipment (cont'd)	
	9. Exhaust & Ventilation	
	Bathroom Exhaust Fans	_____
	Kitchen Exhaust Fans	_____
	Ecology Air Handling Units	_____
	Smoke Exhaust Fans	_____
	Stairwell Pressurization Fans	_____
	Car Park Exhaust Fans	_____
	Fume Hood Exhaust Fans	_____
	10. Fuel Oil System	
	Oil Storage Tank	_____
	Propane Storage Tank	_____
	Oil Pump Sets	_____
	11. Other Equipment	_____
	Motor Starter & MCC's	_____
C132	Ductwork	
	Low Pressure Ductwork	_____
	Medium Pressure Ductwork	_____
	High Pressure Ductwork	_____
	Pre-Fabricated Round Duct	_____
	Pre-Fabricated Round Double Wall Duct	_____
	Sanitary Exhaust Duct	_____
	Specialty Duct Systems:	
	Stainless Steel	_____
	Aluminum	_____
	Acid Resistant	_____
	Flat Oval	_____
	Black Iron	_____
	Pre-Manufactured Plenums	_____
	Duct Lining	_____
	Duct Insulation	_____
	Fire Dampers	_____
	Balancing Dampers	_____
	Sound Attenuators	_____
	Automatic Dampers	_____
	Outside Louvres	_____
	Other	_____

CLARE, RANDALL-SMITH & ASSOCIATES LIMITED

- 8 -

C1   **MECHANICAL**
C13   HVAC
C133   Piping
      High Pressure Steam _____
      Medium Pressure Steam _____
      Low Pressure Steam _____
      Condensate _____
      Hot Water _____
      Chilled Water _____
      Condenser Water _____
      Fuel Oil System _____
      Pre-Insulated Piping System _____
      Fan Coil Drains _____
      Glycol _____
      Snow Melting _____
      Insulation _____
      Other _____
      _____
      _____

C134   Ductwork Terminal Devices
      Variable Air Volume Boxes _____
      Constant Air Volume Boxes _____
      Fan Powered Terminal Boxes _____
      Diffusers _____
      Grilles _____
      Laminar Flow Diffusers _____
      Terminal Humidifiers _____
      HEPA Diffusers _____
      Other _____
      _____

C135   Piping Terminal Devices
      Wall Fin Elements _____
      Wall Fin Enclosures _____
      Runtal Type Heaters _____
      Radiant Heat Panels _____
      Convectors _____
      Radiators _____
      Cabinet Heaters _____
      Unit Heaters _____
      Reheat Coils _____
      Unit Ventilators _____
      Induction Units _____
      Air Curtains _____
      Gas Fired Unit Heaters _____
      Infra-Red Heaters _____
      Radiant Floors _____
      Other _____
      _____
      _____

CLARE, RANDALL-SMITH & ASSOCIATES LIMITED

- 9 -

C1 **MECHANICAL**
C14   CONTROLS
C141   Central Equipment
    Air Compressors   _____
    Computer Hardware   _____
    Computer Software   _____
    Computer Programming   _____
    Other   _____
    _____

C142   Control Points
    Pneumatic Control Points   _____
    DDC Control Points   _____
    Radiation Valves   _____
    VAV Actuators   _____
    Supply and Exhaust Air
     Valves   _____
    Fume Hood Control Modules   _____
    Damper Actuators   _____
    Thermostats
    Monitoring, Sensing &
     Measuring Devices   _____
    Control Valves   _____
    Other   _____
    _____

General Notes on Mechanical: _____

_____
_____
_____
_____
_____
_____
_____
_____
_____
_____
_____
_____
_____
_____
_____
_____

CLARE, RANDALL-SMITH & ASSOCIATES LIMITED

- 10 -

D12   MECHANICAL SITE SERVICES

1. Connection Charges:
   Domestic Water _____
   Fire Line _____
   Sanitary _____
   Storm _____
   Gas _____
   Others _____
2. Outside Services:
   (a) Domestic Water:
       Water Meter and Pit _____
       Pipe Distribution _____
       Back Flow Prevention _____
   (b) Fire Line:
       Fire Hydrants _____
       Post-Indicator Valves _____
       Pipe Distribution _____
       Back Flow Prevention _____
   (c) Sanitary:
       Manholes _____
       Catch Basins _____
       Pipe Collection _____
       Septic Tank and Fields _____
   (d) Storm:
       Manholes _____
       Catch Basins _____
       Pipe Collection _____
       Head Walls _____
       Storm Water Management
         System _____
   (e) Car Park Drainage:
       Manholes _____
       Catch Basins _____
       Area Drains & Trench
       Drains _____
       Pipe Collection _____
   (f) Gas Service:
       Gas Regulating Valves _____
       Pipe Distribution _____
   (g) Miscellaneous Systems:
       Lawn Irrigation _____
       Planter Drains _____
       Steam & Condensate _____
       Hot Water _____
       Chilled Water _____
       Bulk Oxygen Storage _____
       Other _____

CLARE, RANDALL-SMITH & ASSOCIATES LIMITED

- 11 -

C2 ELECTRICAL
C21 SERVICE & DISTRIBUTION
C211 Equipment
    H.V. Switchboard:
        New _____ Existing _____ Revised _____
        Fused _____ Size _____
        Circuit Breakers _____ Size _____
        ■ Request sketch showing make-up of cubicles

    Transformers:
        Size _____ KVA
        Type _____
        Dry _____ Oil _____ Liquid Filled _____
        Fan Cooling _____

    L.V. Switchboard:
        New _____ Existing _____ Revised _____
        Voltage _____ Volts Main Current _____ Amps
        Circuit Breakers _____ Type _____
        Fused _____
        Main Switch or CB Size _____
        No. of Sections _____
        Interrupting Capacity _____
        Ground Fault Protection _____

    Unit Sub-Station:
        Primary Voltage _____ KV
        Type of Incoming Line Section _____
        Type of Transformer _____
        Secondary Voltage _____ Volts
        Type of Outgoing Section _____
        Indoor _____ Outdoor _____
        Interrupting Capacity _____

    Other: _____
        _____

C212 Auxiliary Power Equipment
    Standby Generator:
        New _____ Existing _____
        Size _____ KW Voltage _____ Volts
        Manufacturer _____
        Type of Fuel _____
        Transfer Switch: Type _____ Size _____
        Exhaust System _____
        Indoor _____ Outdoor _____

CLARE, RANDALL-SMITH & ASSOCIATES LIMITED

- 12 -

C2   ELECTRICAL
C21   SERVICE & DISTRIBUTION
C212 Auxiliary Power Equipment (cont'd)
    UPS
        Voltage _____   Static _____   Rotary _____
        Capacity   _____
        Battery Duration   _____
        Maintenance By-Pass   _____
        Load Bank   _____

    Other: _____
                              _____

C213 Distribution
    High Voltage Distribution Feeders:
        Voltage _____ Volts   Type _____   Feeding _____

    Low Voltage Distribution Feeders:
        Voltage _____ Volts   Type _____   Feeding _____

    Bus Duct:
        Copper _____   Aluminum _____   Type _____
        Capacity _____   Amps
        Poles _____   Neutral _____   Feeding _____

    Secondary Feeders:
        Voltage _____ Volts   Type _____
        Transformer Voltage _____ Volts
        Copper _____   Aluminum _____
        ■ Request Single Line Diagram
        ■ Request Riser Diagram

    Power Panels:
        Voltage _____ Volts   Capacity _____ Amps
        Circuit Breakers _____   Fused _____
        Interrupting Capacity _____
        Copper Bus _____ Aluminum Bus _____

    Lighting Panels:
        Voltage _____ Volts   Type _____
        Interrupting Capacity _____
        Copper Bus _____ Aluminum Bus _____

    Co-Ordination Study:
        Scope   _____

    Grounding:
        System ground   _____
        Isolated Ground _____
        Building Ground _____

CLARE, RANDALL-SMITH & ASSOCIATES LIMITED

C2   ELECTRICAL
C21   SERVICE & DISTRIBUTION
C213   Distribution (cont'd)
       Cable Trays:
           Type _____   Material _____

       Other: _____
                                            _____

C214   Motor Controls
       Motor Controllers:
           MCC supplied under Element C1 or C2 _____
           Sep. Starters supplied under Element C1 or C2 _____
           MCC _____   MCC Class _____
           No. of Sections _____   Fused _____   Breakers _____
           Power Factor Correction   _____

       Motor Wiring:
           No. of Motors _____   Voltage _____ Volts   Total H.P. _____
           Type of Air Conditioning   _____
           A/C Voltage _____ Volts

       Other: _____
                                       _____

C22   LIGHTING, DEVICES & HEATING
C221   Lighting
       Lighting Fixtures:
           Voltage _____ Volts   Type of Lamps _____
           Type of Ballast   _____
           Main Fixture   _____
           Type of Lens/Louvre   _____
           Exterior Wall Fixtures   _____
           Special Arch. Lighting   _____

       Theatre Performance Lighting:
           Allowance $_____   No. of Dimmers _____
           Control Consoles   _____
           Quantity of Ltg. Instruments _____

       LV Switching:
           Type _____   Manufacturer _____
           Control _____   No. of Relay Panels _____

       Lighting Control:
           Local Switching   _____
           Dimming   _____
           Occupancy Sensors   _____
           Quick Connect Wiring   _____
           Energy Saving Systems   _____

CLARE, RANDALL-SMITH & ASSOCIATES LIMITED

- 14 -

C2   ELECTRICAL
C22   LIGHTING, DEVICES & HEATING
C221 Lighting (Cont'd)
       Emergency Lighting:
           From Standby Generator   _____
           Battery Units   _____
           Central Battery System   _____

       Other: _____
           _____

C222 Devices
       Branch Wiring:
           Wiring Type   _____
           Device Quality   _____
           Equipment Connections   _____
           Ceiling Grid System   _____
           Isolated Power Centres   _____
           Service Columns   _____
           Furniture Connections   _____
           Service Columns   _____
           Hospital Headwall Units   _____

       Other: _____
           _____

C223 Heating
       Electric Heating:
           Heaters supplied under Element C1 or C2   _____
           Type _____ Voltage _____ Volts
           Controls   _____
           Peak-Load Control   _____
           Duct Heaters   _____

       Building Snow Melting:
           Ramp Heating   _____
           Gutter Tracing   _____
           Pipe Tracing   _____

       Other: _____
           _____

C2 ELECTRICAL
C23 SYSTEMS & ANCILLARIES
C231 Fire Alarm

Fire Alarm:

New _____ Existing _____

Manufacturer _____

Type _____

Zoned _____ Coded _____ Pre-Signal _____

Type of Conduit _____

Smoke Detection _____ Ceiling _____ Ducts _____

P.A. Facility _____

Other: _____

_____

C232 Communications

Telephone:

Type of Service: Empty Conduit _____ Wiring _____

Distribution: Cable Tray _____ Size _____

Floor(s) Affected _____

Conduit _____ Type _____

Equipment by _____

Conduit to: Ceiling _____ Corridor _____

Comm. Closet _____

Ceiling Grid System _____

Internal telephone (PBX):

New _____ Existing _____

Manufacturer _____

No. of Lines _____ No. of Telephones _____

Computer / Data Systems:

System Requirements _____

Networking _____

Cable by _____

Equipment by _____

Radio Systems:

New _____ Existing _____

Empty Conduit System _____

Radio Equipment _____

Antenna _____ Pagers _____

Intercom Systems:

New _____ Existing _____

Manufacturer _____

No. of Stations _____ No. of Lines on Control Station _____

CLARE, RANDALL-SMITH & ASSOCIATES LIMITED

- 16 -

C2   ELECTRICAL
C23   SYSTEMS & ANCILLARIES
C232   Communications (cont'd)
     Enterphone:
       Type   _____
       Manufacturer   _____
       Capacity   _____
       Supplied by   _____

     Other: _____
             _____

C233 Security
     Security:
       Equipment by   _____
       Conduit by   _____
       Wiring by   _____
       Door Monitor   _____
       Motion Detector   _____
       Door Hardware by   _____
       Card Reader   _____

     Closed Circuit TV:
       New _____   Existing _____
       Empty Conduits Only   _____
       Equipment   _____
       Manufacturer   _____
       Locations Served   _____
       Teaching   _____
       Monitoring   _____
       Studio   _____
       Surveillance   _____

     Exterior Services:
       Gate Control   _____

     Other: _____
             _____

C2 ELECTRICAL
C23 SYSTEMS & ANCILLARIES
C234 Other Systems & Ancillaries

Entertainment TV:
New _____   Existing _____
Empty Conduit System   _____
Antenna & Amplifiers   _____
Wiring
Cable TV

Clock & Program:
New _____   Existing _____
Manufacturer   _____
Type   _____
Program   _____

PA System:
New _____   Existing _____
Manufacturer   _____
Type   _____
Areas Serviced   _____
Auditorium System   _____

Lightning Protection:
Type   _____

Laboratory Wiring:
New _____   Existing _____
Type/Function   _____
Area _____   Panels _____
Bench Wiring   _____

Nurse Call:
New _____   Existing _____   No. of Beds _____
Manufacturer   _____
Type   _____

Staff Register:
New _____   Existing _____
Manufacturer   _____
Type   _____
No. of Locations   _____
Operator's Console   _____

C2 **ELECTRICAL**
C23 SYSTEMS & ANCILLARIES
C234 Other Systems & Ancillaries (cont'd)

Underfloor Duct:
Manufacturer _____
Trench Duct _____   Width _____
Header Duct _____
Flush Duct _____   No. of Ducts _____   Sizes _____
Insert Duct _____   No. of Ducts _____   Sizes _____
Fittings in Contract _____   Fittings by Tenant _____
Duct Spacing _____
Poke Thru System _____

Kitchen Wiring:
New _____   Existing _____
Area _____   No. of People Served _____
No. of Connections _____   Total Electrical Load _____

Dictation System:
New _____   Existing _____
No. of Locations _____   Empty Conduits Only _____
Equipment _____
Manufacturer _____

Doctor Paging:
New _____   Existing _____
Manufacturer _____
Type _____

Monitoring Systems:
Physiological Monitoring _____
(Heart, temperature, respiration, blood)
No. of Locations _____   Empty Conduits only _____

Alarms:
Oxygen _____
Nitrous Oxide _____
Drugs & Narcotics _____
Blood Bank _____
Nurse Supervisory Door Alarm _____
Nurses' Residence _____

X-Ray Rooms:
Number _____

Operating Rooms:
Number: _____
Ground Detection System _____

CLARE, RANDALL-SMITH & ASSOCIATES LIMITED

C2 ELECTRICAL
C23 SYSTEMS & ANCILLARIES
C234 Other Systems & Ancillaries (cont'd)
    Miscellaneous Systems:
        Watchman's Tour _____
        Burglar Alarm _____
        Computer Room _____
        R.F. Rooms _____
        System for Hearing
         Impaired _____
        Hand Dryers in Washrooms _____
        Elapsed Time Clock _____

Other: _____
    _____

General:
    Conduit Type _____
    Wire Type _____
    Services/Systems Connections to Other Buildings _____
    _____
    Contingencies _____

General Notes on Electrical: _____

_____
_____
_____
_____

CLARE, RANDALL-SMITH & ASSOCIATES LIMITED

- 20 -

D13 ELECTRICAL SITE SERVICES

Service:

New _____ Existing _____ Revised _____

Voltage _____ Volts Capacity _____ Amps

Interrupting Capacity _____

Cable Size _____ Type _____

Overhead _____

Underground _____ No. & Type of Ducts _____

Distance to Utility Source _____

Manholes _____

Service Tunnel _____

What Will the Utility Supply? _____

Allowance for Connection $ _____

Excavation & Backfill to be included _____

Concrete to be included _____

■ Request Single Line Diagram

Communication Service:

Underground _____ No. & Type of Ducts _____

Distance to Communication Room _____

Area Lighting:

Street _____ Type _____ Length _____

Car Park _____ Type _____ Area _____

No. of Cars _____

Walkways _____ Type _____ Length _____

Architectural _____ Type _____

Voltage _____ Volts Type of Poles _____

Snow Melting:

Location _____ Area _____

Voltage _____ Volts

Type of Control _____

Devices:

Block Heater Outlets _____

Comments: _____

_____

_____

_____

_____

_____

_____

_____

_____

_____

_____

_____

CLARE, RANDALL-SMITH & ASSOCIATES LIMITED

- 21 -

APPENDIX C

The purpose of these two forms is to enable costs to be recorded and controlled during the design development and contract document stages. As an element is designed and costed, or if subsequent revisions are made to it, the cost together with an appropriate description is entered on the Cost Plan Check form. A separate form is used for each element and in some instances, since several designs may be considered for a single element, there can be a number of Cost Plan Check forms for an element. Each form is numbered consecutively but only those which are accepted by the design team and signed by the designer are recorded on the Cost Summary. The element target cost from the cost plan is shown as a reference, together with the most recently updated cost of the element incorporating revisions made since the cost plan was prepared.

As a cost check is approved the amount shown on the Cost Plan Check form is entered onto the Cost Summary. The Summary shows, in chronological order, the amount of each cost check, the numbers of Cost Plan Checks, the elements to which they apply, the amount of each cost check, the revision if necessary to the Design Allowance, the revised total budget upon approval of the cost check, and the date when it was approved.

COST PLAN CHECK

Project No. _____

Project _____   Check No. _____

Element _____   Date _____

Description:

_____

_____

_____

_____

_____

_____

_____

_____

_____

_____

_____

_____

_____

_____

_____

_____

Original Element Target Cost $ _____

Previous Revised Element Target Cost $ _____

New Revised Element Target Cost $ _____

Other Elements affected by this Check _____

Comments / Decision:

_____

_____

_____

_____

_____

_____

_____

_____

Signed _____

Architect / Engineer

Project No. _____

COST SUMMARY

Project _____ Page _____

Check No.	Element	Amount	Revised Design Allowance	Revised Total	Date

Bibliography

Bathurst, Peter E. and David A. Butler: *Building Cost Control Techniques and Economics,* William Heinemann Ltd. London, 1964.

Canadian Institute of Steel Construction and Canadian Steel Industries Construction Council: *A Project Analysis Approach to Buildings,* Toronto, 1976

Dell'Isolla, Alphonse J.: *Value Engineering in the Construction Industry,* Construction Publishing Company, Inc.

Dent, Colin: *Construction Cost Appraisal,* George Goodwin Limited, London, 1975.

Department of Health, Education and Welfare: *Life Cycle Budgeting and Costing,* Washington, Vol. I, 1975; Vol. II, 1976; Vol. III, 1976; Vol. IV, 1976.

Ferry, Douglas J.: *Cost Planning of Buildings,* London 1964.

Hillebrandt, Patricia: *Economic Theory and the Construction Industry,* MacMillan, London, 1974.

Hutton, G.H. and A.D.G. Devonald, editors: *Value in Building,* Applied Science Publishers Ltd., London 1974.

Kent, Frederick C. and Maude E.: *Compound Interest and Annuity Tables,* McGraw-Hill Book Company, New York, 1963.

Lichfield, Nathaniel: *Economics of Planned Development,* The Estates Gazette Ltd., London, 1974.

Mansfield, G.L.: *Bidding and Estimating Procedures for Construction,* Reston Publishing Company, Inc., Reston, Virginia, 1983.

Ministry of Public Building and Works: *Cost Control in Building Design,* Her Majesty's Stationery Office, London, 1968.

Nisbet, James: *Estimating and Cost Control,* B.T. Batsford Ltd. 1968.

Parker, Donald E. and Alphonse Dell'Isola: *Project Budgeting for Buildings,* Van Nostrand Reinhold, New York, 1991.

Steacey, Richard: *Canadian Real Estate: How to Make it Pay* MacLean-Hunter, Toronto.

Stone, P.A.: *Building Design Evaluation: Cost-in-Use,* E. & F.N. Spon, London, 1967.

Strung, Joseph: *Introduction to Modern Real Estate Investment Analysis and Valuation,* Strung Real Estate Limited, Toronto, 1976.

Index